McGRAW-HILL PUBLICATIONS IN INDUSTRIAL ARTS

Chris H. Groneman, *Consulting Editor*

GENERAL METALS

These projects, which represent all areas of metalwork, have won
Ford Motor Company Industrial Arts Awards.

General Metals

BY JOHN L. FEIRER

Professor and Head, Industrial Arts Department
Western Michigan College, Kalamazoo, Michigan

8941

McGRAW-HILL BOOK COMPANY, INC.

New York　　Toronto　　London

GENERAL METALS

Library of Congress Catalog Card Number: 51–12564

VI

THE MAPLE PRESS COMPANY, YORK, PA.

Preface

General Metals has been written to satisfy a need for a comprehensive text in the field of metalworking which will fulfill both the spirit and the letter of a modern industrial-arts program. The book is divided into eight main sections, including bench metal and wrought iron, sheet metal, art metal and jewelry, forging, heat-treating, foundry, welding and machine shop, and three additional sections: one covering the introduction to general metalwork, one on metal and metal products, and another of suggested projects. Each unit of each section has been designed to include the basic tools, materials, processes, and related information for a specific step in metalworking.

The book is planned for a general metal shop, for the general metal area of a general shop, and for the home craftsman. While beginning classes may do creative work in only the areas of bench, sheet, and art metal, these students will have an opportunity to read about all areas of metalwork. As time and experience permits, students may make representative projects in the other areas.

Besides covering the manipulative processes of metalwork, this book deals with the following important details:

the principles of good design, illustrated by a representative group of well-designed projects; general occupational information; and suggestions concerning recreational opportunities in each area. Safety, which is all-important in shopwork, is given both special attention and specific application in each unit of work. The book stresses the illustrative approach to instruction, and each illustration has been carefully selected for that purpose. Consumer information about metal and metal products, so meaningful in our modern industrial society, is given constant emphasis.

The following companies have been most generous in their assistance: Air Reduction Sales Company; Allis-Chalmers Manufacturing Co.; Aluminum Company of America; American Gas Furnace Co.; American Handicrafts Co.; American Iron and Steel Institute; E. F. Atkins & Company; Atlas Press Company; Behr-Manning Corporation; Berkroy Products Inc.; Boice-Crane Co.; Brodhead-Garrett Co.; Brown & Sharpe Mfg. Co.; Carborundum Company; Carnegie-Illinois Steel Corporation; Casting Specialties; Chrysler Corporation; Cincinnati Shaper Company; Cleveland Twist Drill Co.; Copper and Brass Research Association; Henry Diss-

v

ton and Sons; William Dixon Incorporated; Ford Motor Company; General Motors Corporation; Greenfield Tap and Die Corporation; Handy and Harman; Heller Brothers Company; Hobart Brothers Co.; Georg Jensen Inc.; Johnson Gas Appliance Co.; Kester Solder Co.; Linde Air Products Company; Lufkin Rule Co.; Metal Goods Corporation; Molla, Inc.; Montgomery Ward; Morse Twist Drill and Machine Co.; National Safety Council; Niagara Machine and Tool Works; Peck, Stow & Wilcox Co.; Pheoll Manufacturing Company; Pioneer Bait and Tackle Co.; Racine Tool and Machine Co.; Joseph T. Ryerson and Son, Inc., (for Unit 59); and Reynolds Metals Company; School Shop Magazine; Stanley Tools; L. S. Starrett Co.; Sunbeam Corporation; United States Steel Corporation; R. Wallace and Sons Manufacturing Co.; Wells Manufacturing Corporation; and Willy-Overland Corporation. The author wishes to acknowledge, also, the assistance given him by the following individuals: Lindsay Farnan, Edward Huttenga, Tom Ross, and Norman Russell.

JOHN L. FEIRER

Contents

Contents

Editor's Foreword

Present-day life in America is one of industrial and technical activity. Ingenuity, resourcefulness, and competitive spirit are largely responsible for the technical advances that are achieved daily. Scientific progress depends upon the skills of the men and women engaged in all phases of industrial activity. The speed and efficiency developed by these skilled people are traced to a proper understanding and appreciation of fundamental processes and materials.

No other people in the world have the distinct advantage of living with and enjoying the products fabricated from metal to such an extent as those in America. Therefore, in order to have an adjusted approach to modern living, it is desirable for the individual to know about and to be able to work with this challenging medium.

Education, according to some thinkers, is the liberation of capacity. To them the end of education is to produce well-balanced and many-sided interests. Teaching is defined by others as the awakening of another's mind, and the training of its faculties to a normal self-activity. To educate the individual means to adjust him to those elements in his environment that are of concern to modern life, and to develop, organize,

and train his powers so that he may make efficient and proper use of them. Considering these functions of education, and the closely related functions of books, the tools of knowledge, one comes to the realization of the importance of a series of books such as the McGraw-Hill Publications in Industrial Arts.

Industrial arts is understood by many to be one of the practical arts; it is a form of nonvocational education which has for its purpose the providing of experiences in, and information about, the tools and materials incident generally to the home and the manufacturing industries. It also affords to the student the opportunity to function in class organizations simulating practices of industrial nature where satisfaction can be achieved through success in developing attitudes of cooperation, dependability, punctuality, orderly procedures, and analytical thinking.

General Metals, one of the first books in the new McGraw-Hill Publications in Industrial Arts, introduces a junior or senior high-school-age boy or girl to a full year or more of orientation, experiences, and necessary information in the areas of ornamental iron, bench metal, sheet metal, art metal and jewelry, heat treating, forging, foundry, welding, and machine shop.

The student is assisted in this orientation to the general metalworking field by having the opportunity to study or delve into related information pertaining to the numerous types of metals, sources of them, manufacturing processes, occupational opportunities, safety practices, and learning to understand and practice the fundamentals and characteristics of good design.

The book is prepared in such a manner that it serves as a ready reference for the student. It is adapted to the life adjustment philosophy of the democratic principles by aiding in the development of worth-while and useful citizens who are capable of exercising initiative and ingenuity and of using knowledge in order to gain the many fine attributes so desirable in our American youth. Comenius said that education is the development of the whole man, and the thought given in the preparation of this book has consciously directed its purpose to that worthy goal.

This textbook is enriched by the many expressive illustrations which point up with clarity the processes necessary in working with metals. It is unique in the organization of the subject matter. It should prove a real contribution to industrial arts literature.

Dr. John L. Feirer, the author, received his basic industrial education from one of the outstanding colleges in this field where he supplemented his previous interesting industrial experiences in the metalworking industries.

He continued his formal education until he was awarded the doctorate degree. He is one of the nationally recognized leaders in the field of industrial-arts education, and is the author or coauthor of several widely accepted texts and project books in the industrial-arts field. His contributions to professional magazines are timely and have stimulated constructive thinking toward the improvement of industrial-arts programs.

The teacher who uses *General Metals* as a basic guide will find it to be a very fundamental, practical, and adaptable base from which he can expand his course in metals to one of vital interest to himself and to those in his classes. The flexibility of the arrangement of material adds zest to the course.

The editor and the author hope that this publication will fill a very real need for the student by supplying for him many exploratory and avocational activities. They trust that it will assist him to realize and appreciate more fully some of the impact and significance exerted by metalworking in the industrial society of today.

McGraw-Hill Publications in Industrial Arts is a functional and practical series of books designed for general educational objectives and for the benefit of both the student and the teacher. It is the purpose of the series to present a well-planned series of texts, written by authors of national significance, in the broad areas of industrial arts which will be of aid to a planned effectuality in total living.

CHRIS H. GRONEMAN

GENERAL METALS

Section I. METALWORKING

Unit 1. Introduction to Metals

The general field of metalworking is well represented in the manufacturing industries in the United States. More people are employed and more products in money value are produced in metalworking than in any other industrial field. Metal and electricity are the keys to our way of life, and since most electrical products are made of metal, the field becomes doubly important. The chances are more than one in ten that you will be working in the metal industry some day.

General metal covers all fields of metalworking: bench metal, sheet metal, art metal and jewelry, forging, heat-treating, foundry, welding, and machine shop. The work of the men in these fields varies greatly. (Fig. 1-1). Foundrymen, for example, use tools that are entirely

Fig. 1-1. This expert metalworker and his helper are making a complicated layout on a large piece of steel. The machinist is studying the blueprint and using many layout tools, much like those you will use. He cannot afford to make a mistake, so he is carefully following the plans and blueprints. You must learn to do the same.

1

unlike those the sheet-metal worker needs. The welder must possess skills quite different from those of the machinist. All these workers are important, however, in the production of metal products. Consider the automobile industry, for instance. It must have foundrymen to make all the castings, men to forge other parts that require great strength, machinists to operate the various machines that shape parts, heat-treaters to control the quality of the metal, sheet-metal workers to form the body parts, and welders and bench-metal workers to assemble and finish the automobiles.

In each area of metalworking there are many kinds of careers and jobs. Industry needs engineers and skilled technicians to plan and supervise the work, skilled craftsmen for the difficult operations, semiskilled men to operate production machines, and unskilled workmen to do many of the routine jobs. If you have

Fig. 1-2. This box of tools, most of which are handmade, provided an outstanding future for the metalsmith who made them. Hand tools are so important in metalworking that learning to use them correctly is essential to success in any mechanical occupation.

visited the laboratories in which Thomas Edison, Henry Ford, or Walter Chrysler worked, you know that each was a fine metalworker possessing a wide variety of skills (Fig. 1-2).

Metal products, and there are literally thousands, amount to approximately 20 tons of metal in use for every man, woman, and child in the United States. All of us buy and use many kinds of metal products, from toys to kitchen utensils, bicycles, and cars. We should be interested in their design and in the quality of craftsmanship that goes into them. We should know how to maintain and repair them to make them last. Many of you whose occupations will be in fields other than metalwork will find fascinating hobbies in such activities as etching, spinning, modelmaking, and jewelry.

Before you can begin to make a project in metalwork, there are some things you should know, such as how to work safely in the shop, how to select and design projects, how to read drawings, how to plan a project, how to select metals, and how to measure and to make layouts. When you have learned these things, you are ready for the wonderful experience of fashioning something worth while of metal. While you may not have the time or experience to construct projects in each of the areas, you will have a chance to learn about each field.

Discussion Topics

1. In what way are electricity and general metal related?
2. Name the fields of metalworking represented in general metal.

3. Name some of the occupational classifications of metalworkers and tell what each requires of the worker.
4. Give a definition of "general metal."

5. Will the beginner be able to construct projects in every area?
6. What information has been included in each section of this book?

Unit 2. Safety in the Shop

Your experiences in the shop will be more profitable and pleasant if they are not marred by an accident, however small. It is important to learn how to be both a good and a safe worker. The best way is to do each thing carefully and correctly, just as it is described in this book or as it is demonstrated by your instructor. Do not be the one to have an accident by doing the wrong thing "just this time" or by hurrying and not following proper procedure.

The shop is organized in such a way that it is safe for work. Notice that all of the machines you may be allowed to use are carefully guarded and that everything is in order. It is your responsibility to help in the maintenance of the shop so that it will be safe for all. The shop is a place to work—horseplay is dangerous to you and to your friends.

The Way You Dress

Dressing safely means wearing the right kind of protective clothing. Make sure that your hair is kept short or that you wear a close-fitting cap. It is extremely dangerous to bend over a buffing wheel, grinder, or metal lathe if your hair is long. *Roll up your sleeves, tuck in your tie, and wear a shop coat or an apron* (Fig. 2-1). Also, remove jewelry; the

band of a watch, for example, can easily get caught and add to your injury. Special protective clothing is needed for welding, forging, and foundry.

Protecting Your Eyes

You have only two eyes and you cannot buy a new pair. Be very careful, particularly wherever there is danger of flying metal chips or abrasives. When grinding and buffing metal, you will require special protection. Most modern grinders are equipped with eye safety shields, but, if not, be sure to wear goggles or an eye shield. Special glasses or shields are needed for many operations in foundry, welding, and machine shop.

Fig. 2-1. Here are two men who don't know how to dress properly for work. Molten metal is something you cannot fool with. The tie on the lathe operator is sure to catch in the machine, and if he escapes without hanging himself, he'll be lucky.

HAND TOOLS

FIG. 2-2. Another do-wronger. He uses the wrong tools and every one is in such poor condition that he couldn't use them right if he tried.

Most small accidents are caused by using hand tools incorrectly or by failing to keep them in good working condition (Fig. 2-2). Check to see that the hammer heads and screw-driver handles are tight, that the mushroom heads are ground off the cold chisel, center punch, and other small tools, and that the pliers, screw drivers, and metal shears are in good working condition.

Some of the common small injuries are cuts from burred edges of metal or scraps lying around, pinches from pliers or snips, and burns from hot metal or hot tools.

FIG. 2-3. Here is your chance to see how many safety practices are being violated. If you cannot find 10, your knowledge of safety is incomplete.

MACHINES

In the more advanced work you will be permitted to use some of the machines in the sheet-metal, welding, and machine shops. You cannot use these, however, until you have had the proper experience in hand-tool work and proper instruction in the use of each machine. Remember this: *Always follow the safety precautions described in each unit.* Never allow anyone to stand around or near the machine you are using. Many accidents are caused by the worker's being distracted when someone comes too near the machine (Fig. 2-3). The following story is true. Two boys were cutting pieces of metal that were too small on a squaring shears. One boy was in front of the machine and the other in back of it. The boy behind the machine had his fingers under the guillotine blade just as the boy in front lowered the blade. The boy lost a thumb.

When using any machine, always keep your hands and fingers away from moving parts. Never attempt to hold a piece of metal in your hand while it is being machined in the drill press, lathe, or shaper. Never use measuring tools on metal while it is being machined. It takes only one accident to ruin your life.

TREATMENT OF INJURIES

No matter how small the injury or burn,

Fig. 2-4. The "characters" in need of first aid may look comical, but it is no joke when it happens to *you*. What is wrong with each treatment?

treat it properly and immediately. Report to your instructor to receive first aid, and if necessary, he will send you to the school nurse or to a doctor. A small burn, a metal sliver, or a cut can easily cause blood poisoning, and a piece of metal in the eye can cause blindness (Fig. 2-4). Don't say it doesn't happen. Each year there are 64,000 eye injuries in schools and industrial shops. Do not add to this number.

Remember these basic rules of safety and practice them:

1. *Dress properly.*
2. *Know your job.*
3. *Do it correctly.*

Discussion Topics

1. What is the proper way to dress in the shop?
2. In what ways can the eyes be protected? Why is this necessary?
3. What special care should be taken of hand tools to avoid accidents?
4. Why is it dangerous to use an unfamiliar machine?
5. When using a machine, what special safety precautions should you keep in mind at all times?
6. What would you do in case of accident in the shop?

Unit 3. Good Design

Every product that is made must first be designed. In the beginning, the design is only an idea in the mind of the de-

Fig. 3-1. Is this the automobile design of the future? The trend is toward simplicity, greater streamlining, and an appearance of sleekness which makes the car appear to be moving even when standing still.

signer; then it is a rough sketch on a piece of paper; then it is a finished drawing in three or more views; then a model; and finally the finished product (Fig. 3-1). The article may be either well designed or poorly designed, depending on how the elements of design are arranged and how well the principles of good design are applied.

There are certain basic elements in design that make up the over-all appearance, just as there are certain basic elements that make alloys. For example, zinc and copper are mixed together to make brass, and the way it is done and the proportion of the metals used determine the kind of brass obtained. This is also true of the basic elements of design, such as the following:

1. *Line.* A line may be straight, curved, crooked, or a combination of these.

2. *Shape.* Shape is the result of lines. It is the appearance of an object from one view. For example, the outline of an automobile from the sides looks like 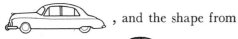 , and the shape from the front looks like .

3. *Mass.* Mass is the three dimensional element of a design. It is the appearance of an object showing its width, height, and length all at once.

4. *Tone.* Tone is the difference in lightness and darkness, or shading. This may be produced by shadows, by color, or by the materials used.

5. *Color.* Color can be pleasing or distasteful depending upon the way it is used. In metalwork, color may be part of the metal itself or it can be applied to it with paint, lacquer, or some other type of finish.

6. *Texture.* Texture is the character of the surface. For example, metal that is peened has a different texture from metal that is scratchbrushed.

To achieve good design there are certain basic principles that must be followed, applying these elements. These are:

1. *Balance.* An article is in balance when it appears to have equal weight or areas on either side, like the balance of a scale. This does not mean that two sides must be the same size, since balance can be obtained by using different materials or different colors or by having the parts at different distances from the eye. There are two kinds of balance, formal and informal (Fig. 3-2).

FIG. 3-2. This metal tray represents *formal balance,* since the two sides are identical. Often, however, an object can still be in balance when the two sides are unlike but appear to be of about equal weight or size.

FIG. 3-3. This beautiful handmade sterling bowl is the work of one of the world's greatest silversmiths. Its beauty is due, to a large extent, to the *proportion* of the various parts. A larger or smaller base might have made it appear clumsy or top-heavy.

2. *Proportion.* This is the relationship between the sizes of the various parts of an object. For example, if you place a large shade on a small lamp, the whole lamp is out of proportion, but the same shade on a larger base of the proper size

Fig. 3-4. The principle of *rhythm,* or *repetition,* is strikingly represented in this metal building. How many different parts of the structure can you count that show rhythm?

would appear to be in good proportion (Fig. 3-3).

3. *Rhythm,* or *repetition.* The regular repeating of a line or shape gives the article a pleasing appearance and a feeling of rhythm (Fig. 3-4).

Fig. 3-5. This baseball and football stadium is a good example of *harmony.* The parts of the structure are in pleasing relation to one another.

4. *Harmony.* An object may be said to possess harmony when the relationship of its parts provides a pleasing combination (Fig. 3-5).

5. *Emphasis.* A certain part of an article may be emphasized by the use of accents. The emphasis may be merely in the shape of the object, in the use of color, or in decoration (Fig. 3-6).

TRENDS IN DESIGN

Over the years there has been a very definite trend in the design of articles toward simplicity and uncluttered line,

Fig. 3-6. The attractive cast parts on the back of this chair are points of *emphasis.* You see them immediately, for they attract the eye and add greatly to the beauty of the chair.

especially in metal products. When you compare articles of several years ago with those designed today, you can readily see this change (Fig. 3-7). The primary reasons are that articles that are simple and not overdecorated are easier to mass-produce, more efficient in use, and easier to maintain. The beginning craftsman should remember this, since he has a tendency to overdecorate and to make the project too ornate.

You may not have the opportunity to design projects, at least not in the beginning. However, you will be selecting designs for them. Do not make the mistake of thinking that all the projects to be found in books, magazines, and shops, are examples of good design. Learn to have a critical eye, to be a good judge, and to reject poor design.

When selecting a project, keep in mind:

1. *Selection for use.* First of all an article should be something you can use. In other words, it must have some functional value. Look at the list in Table 3-1 and see how many things you or your family need.

2. *Selection of metals.* You need to known something about metal: how it will react to forming, bending, shaping, and soldering, and whether it is suited to the particular article you want to make. For example, copper cannot be used with acid foods unless it is plated or tinned.

3. *Construction of the article.* You should know something about construction details. How is the article to be bent? How can it be joined? Can it be soldered, riveted, or joined with seams?

FIG. 3-7. Here we see the changes 15 years have made in bicycle design. In how many ways have safety, utility, convenience, and comfort been improved in the later model?

Old   New

TABLE 3-1. WHAT TO DESIGN IN METALWORK

Andirons
Anvils
Ash trays
Back rests
Baggage racks
Barbecue pits
Bed lamps, rests, and
  trays
Bells
Belt clasps and
  ornaments
Bobsleds
Book ends and racks
Book stands
Bookmarks
Bowls
Boxes
Bridge lamps
Bridge tables
Broom holders
Bud vases
Buttons
Calendars
Calipers
Candlesticks
Centerpieces, table
Chairs, camp
Chessmen
Chimes
Christmas
  decorations
Christmas-tree
  stands
Cigarette holders
Clock cases
Coasters
Coffeepots
Cookery utensils
Costume jewelry
Cribbage boards
Crosses
Cups
Cutlery
Desk lamps
Diving helmets

Dog harness
Door knockers
Doorstops
Drawer pulls
Dustpans
Escutcheons, keyhole
Fire screens
Fishing-tackle
  boxes
Floor lamps
Flower holders
Foot scrapers
Footstools
Fountain-pen
  holders
Funnels
Game boards
Gongs
Grilles
Gun racks
Hack saws
Hammers
Hampers
Hat racks
Hinges
Hooks
Ice buckets
Ice cutters
Incense burners
Initials
Inkstands
Jacks
Jewelry
Key cases
Key rings
Kitchen furniture
Kitchen utensils
Kite reels
Knife racks
Knockers
Ladders
Lamps
Laundry carts
Lawn ornaments
Letter knives

Levels
Lighting fixtures
Machine tools
Magazine racks and
  stands
Mailboxes
Marking gauges
Matchbox holders
Medals
Memorandum pads
Metal flowers
Minnow boxes
Muffin stands
Mugs
Music boxes
Music stands
Nail boxes
Name plates
Napkin rings
Necktie racks
Newspaper holders
Notebooks
Nut dishes
Nutcrackers
Paper knives
Paperweights
Penholders
Picnic outfits
Picture frames
Pipe racks
Pitchers
Plant boxes
Plant brackets
Plant stands
Plaques
Plates, metal
Powder boxes
Reels
Rings (jewelry)
Salt shakers
Sconces
Scoops
Scrapbooks
Screw drivers
Scribers

Sea chests
Shelves
Shoe cabinets
Shoe-polishing
  stands
Shoe racks
Shoescrapers
Silhouettes
Ski racks
Smoking stands
Spears, fishing
Stationery holders
Stools
String holders
Sugar-and-cream
  sets
Sundials
T-square
Table lamps
Tables, glass-top
Tableware
Tea bells
Tea wagons
Teapots
Telephone stands
Tongs
Toolboxes and tool
  racks
Tools
Toothbrush holders
Towel racks
Toys
Tray stands
Trays
Trowels
Vises
Wall brackets and
  shelves
Wastebaskets
Watch fobs
Weather vanes
Wells, ornamental
Wheelbarrows, toy
Wood baskets and
  boxes

1. Can you explain what makes a thing well designed?
2. Name the elements of design. Find an example of each in a magazine, newspaper or project manual.

3. Define the six principles of design.
4. What accounts for the trend toward simplicity?
5. How can you develop your taste for, and appreciation of, good design?

Unit 4. Designing a Project

Whether or not you design a project of your own, it is very helpful to go through the steps the designer follows. Before beginning the design, keep in mind what the project is to be used for. A lamp should be designed so as to enclose the cord in the base, to be convenient in use, and to give good light. Book ends are meant to hold up books without scratching the table or desk top. A cold chisel must actually cut metal; one made of mild steel might look good but would be worthless.

Let us suppose that you want to design a lamp:

1. What is it to be used for: reading, decoration, hall lighting, note writing, sewing, or studying?

2. In what kind of room is it to be placed: a study, a modern living room, an early American kitchen, or a traditional living room?

3. What size and shape should it be? You should, if possible, obtain the lamp shade first, or make certain that the desired size and shape can be bought or made so that the complete lamp will be well proportioned and harmonious.

4. What materials will be used: ferrous or nonferrous sheet metal, a cast base, tubing, or pipe? Is one kind of metal to be used or a combination of metals and other materials such as wood or plastic?

5. How is it to be constructed? Will it be hollow and assembled by soldering or riveting, will it be turned on a lathe or cast in the foundry?

With these questions answered, make a rough sketch of the several designs (Fig. 4-1). Indicate approximate sizes, and if the shade is available, hold it up to judge the proportion, size, and shape. Make any necessary corrections. (If the project will look different from two sides, sketch and check both views.)

Select the sketch that looks best, and make a detailed working drawing to show the size and kind of material and all construction details. The design should be carefully checked to eliminate errors. If possible, lay out the design on a piece of heavy paper, and cut it out to see what it looks like.

Even after all of these things are done, you must construct the project and use

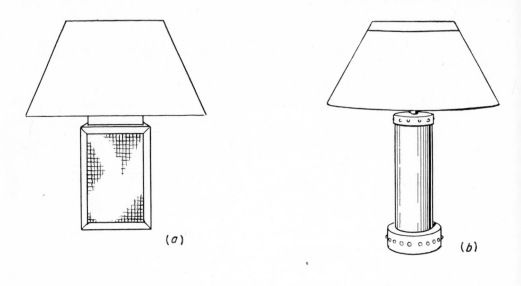

(a)

(b)

(c)

(d)

Fig. 4-1. Sketches of various kinds of lamps which could be developed into good designs. The author liked the lower one (c), so he made a finished drawing, a plan, and then constructed the lamp.

it for a while before you can be sure it is satisfactory (Fig. 4-2). That is why it is wise to select a good design that has already been constructed until you have had some experience and have learned to appreciate good design.

Discussion Topics

1. What are some things that will help you in designing a project?
2. How would you go about designing a simple project? Choose one and list the steps necessary to its design.
3. Clip out examples of good design from an old magazine and tell in what ways they are pleasing.
4. Why is it better for the beginner to select a project rather than to design one?

FIG. 4-2. The finished lamp represents balance, good proportion between shade and base, and harmony. A 2-inch brass pipe is used for the base and ⅛-inch brass tubing for arms. →

Unit 5. Reading Drawings and Prints

Before the metalsmith can begin the actual building of a project, he must be able to read the drawing or print and be able to transfer the measurements from the drawing to the metal. Sometimes he must also sketch and draw the object, especially when he is designing his own. Drawing is a universal language that everyone should understand.

PICTORIAL DRAWINGS

In many books and magazines there are drawings that look like photographs, representing the article as it appears to the eye (Fig. 5-1). These are called *pictorial drawings* and are not satisfactory for construction purposes since they do not ordinarily represent the true shape or size of the parts.

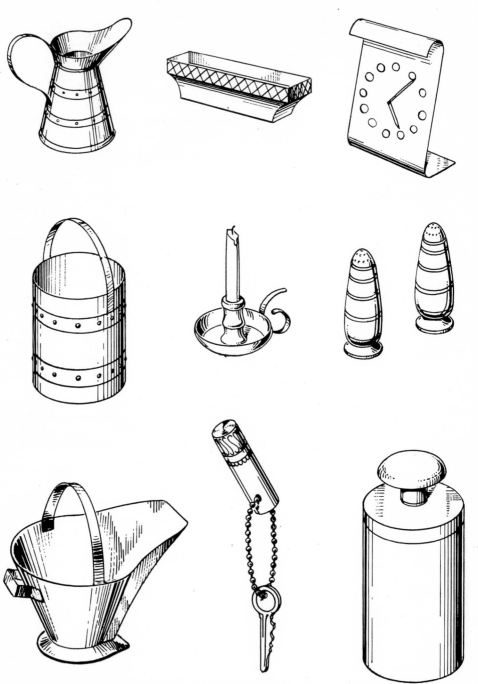

Fig. 5-1. Some attractive metal projects. They give you a good idea of what the object will look like, but such a sketch should not be used for construction.

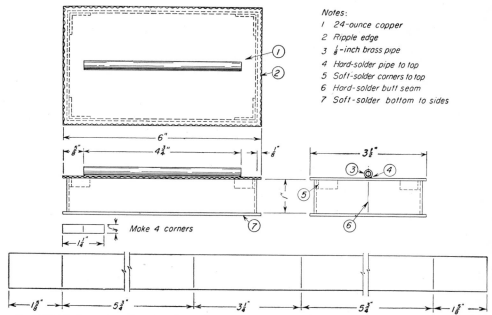

Notes:
1. 24-ounce copper
2. Ripple edge
3. $\frac{1}{8}$-inch brass pipe
4. Hard-solder pipe to top
5. Soft-solder corners to top
6. Hard-solder butt seam
7. Soft-solder bottom to sides

Make 4 corners

Fig. 5-2. A three-view drawing shows how a trinket box will appear from the front, top, and right side. Only rarely is the left side or the bottom shown.

Working Drawings
(Orthographic Projection)

Drawings that are used for construction purposes are called *working drawings* or *orthographic projections* (Fig. 5-2). A three-view drawing is made with the front view in the lower left-hand corner of the page, the top view above it, and the right side or end to the right of the front view. In this way, all parts of the article are represented in their true size and shape. Most drawings you will be using are of this type.

Meaning of Lines

Each line in a drawing has a certain meaning, and it is important in reading a drawing and making sketches to observe and draw these lines correctly (Fig. 5-3).

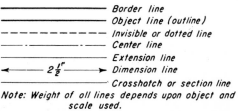

Border line
Object line (outline)
Invisible or dotted line
Center line
Extension line
$2\frac{1}{2}''$ Dimension line
Crosshatch or section line

Note: Weight of all lines depends upon object and scale used.

Fig. 5-3. The lines of your drawing are like the alphabet of our language. Here is the alphabet of lines. Each line must be represented correctly in order that the drawing can be interpreted properly.

Dimensions

The dimensions on the drawing show the measurements of various parts. There are certain standards for dimensioning such details as holes, arcs, angles, and screw threads (Fig. 5-4).

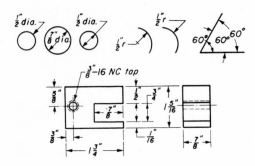

Pattern Development

Sheet-metal objects that are bent up into shape must first be drawn out on a flat surface, and this is called *pattern development* or *making a stretch-out* of the object.

Discussion Topics

1. What is a "pictorial drawing"? Why would you not use it for building a project?
2. What kind of drawing should be used?
3. Sketch out a drawing of a simple project, naming the views.

Unit 6. Making Projects of Metal

There is a great deal to be learned about metal. You can hope to become acquainted with only the more common metals and alloys at first. A metal is one of nature's basic elements. An alloy is a combination of two or more elements. A knowledge of metals is needed since each is different in color, working characteristics, cost, and use.

Metals and alloys can be divided into two groups: the ferrous (iron), which have a base of iron, and the nonferrous, which contain no iron. Some common ferrous metals and alloys are wrought iron, cast iron, mild steel, tool steel, and alloy steel. The common nonferrous metals are copper, aluminum, tin, zinc, lead, nickel, and silver, and the alloys we hear about most often are brass, bronze, nickel silver (german silver), and pewter (bri-

tannia metal). *In common practice, the word "metal" applies to both a metal or an alloy whether it is ferrous or nonferrous.*

Properties of Metal

The following are some of the common properties of metal which every metalworker must understand:

1. *Hardness.* Hardness is the property that makes metal resist penetration or keeps it from bending and being distorted. The hardness of most metals is increased by hammering, by rolling, or by working in other ways. Steels and certain kinds of aluminum alloys can be hardened by heat-treating. See Unit 48, "Heat-treating Steels," page 155.

2. *Brittleness* is the property that causes metal to crack or to break without

changing its shape. Certain kinds of cast iron can be broken easily by being dropped or hammered. Hardness and brittleness are very closely related since hard metals are more brittle than soft metals.

3. *Malleability* is the ability to be stretched or extended by hammering. It permits metals to be bent or shaped either cold or hot as in forging. Copper, for example, is very malleable and is therefore often chosen for trays and bowls, while nickel silver is not very malleable and would be a poor choice for formed projects.

4. *Ductility* is the property which enables metal to be drawn out thin without breaking. Since wire and tubing must be drawn, the metals selected for them have high ductility.

5. *Fusibility* is the characteristic of liquefying when heated. This is very important in joining metals by soldering or by welding.

6. *Corrosiveness* is the characteristic of deteriorating or wearing away when exposed to the elements. While most steels are very corrosive, wrought iron is not. Therefore, water pipes and water mains that are made of wrought iron may last hundreds of years.

Common Nonferrous or Art Metals

All nonferrous metals are measured in one of three ways: (1) copper sheets are sold by the weight per square foot, that is, a 24-ounce copper weighs $1\frac{1}{2}$ pounds per square foot; (2) metal such

FIG. 6-1. Try the various slots in this disk until the metal slips into one of them. The numbers stamped near the opening indicate the gauge. There is a different disk gauge for ferrous and nonferrous metals, one stamped U.S. Standard and the other Brown & Sharpe or American.

as aluminum is indicated by the decimal equivalent, that is, 0.125 aluminum would be $\frac{1}{8}$ inch thick; (3) the Brown & Sharpe gauge, or American gauge, is the standard for most nonferrous metals (Fig. 6-1). See Table 6-1.

1. *Copper* is a warm reddish-brown color. It is the universal choice of most beginning craftsmen for art metalwork. It has excellent cold- and hot-working qualities, can be annealed easily, solders well, resists corrosion, and will take an excellent polish and finish. It does not machine easily, however, and you will find it more difficult to cut threads on a copper rod than on a mild-steel rod.

2. *Brass* is one of the most popular of the copper alloys. There are many kinds of brass, each with different working qualities. Two of the most common are

TABLE 6-1

Number of Gauges	American or Brown & Sharpe	U.S. Standard for plate
	For wire and sheet of copper and other metals than steel	Legalized standard for iron and steel
11	0.0907	0.1250
12	0.0808	0.1094
13	0.0720	0.0938
14	0.0641	0.0781
15	0.0571	0.0703
16	0.0508	0.0625
17	0.0453	0.0563
18	0.0403[a]	0.0500
19	0.0359	0.0438
20	0.0320[b]	0.0375
21	0.0285	0.0344
22	0.0253[c]	0.0313
23	0.0226	0.0281
24	0.0201[d]	0.0250
25	0.0179	0.0219
26	0.0159	0.0188
27	0.0142	0.0172
28	0.0126	0.0156
29	0.0113	0.0141
30	0.0100	0.0125
31	0.0089	0.0109
32	0.0080	0.0102
33	0.0071	0.0094
34	0.0063	0.0086
35	0.0056	0.0078
36	0.0050	0.0070
37	0.0045	0.0066
38	0.0040	0.0063
39	0.0035	
40	0.0031	

[a] 32 ounces
[b] 24 ounces
[c] 20 ounces
[d] 16 ounces

commercial bronze, which contains 10 per cent zinc, and *red brass,* which contains 15 per cent zinc; both of these are excellent for making art metal and jewelry projects. Red brass has a color almost identical to gold. Brass is highly ductile and can be made into wire and other drawn shapes. It is a good base for plating. Copper and brass make excellent contrasting color combinations.

3. *Bronze,* which is reddish-gold in color, is an alloy of copper and tin with, in some cases, a little aluminum. It is a beautiful metal for decorative castings, plaques, and similar articles that are always popular projects. It works well cold, soft-solders easily, and can be welded or brazed.

4. *Nickel silver* is light pink to silver-white in color and is sometimes called *german silver.* It is an alloy of copper, nickel, and zinc. The more nickel it contains, the whiter it is. A combination of 65 per cent copper, 18 per cent nickel, and 17 per cent zinc is used for art metal and jewelry work. This grade is a good imitation of sterling silver but is quite brittle and cannot be hammered into shapes. It is easy to solder, it bends quite well and is a good metal for etching, but it discolors. This alloy is used as the base for all good silver-plate tableware.

5. *Pewter, or britannia metal,* has a pleasing gray color and is 92 per cent tin, 6 per cent antimony, and 2 per cent copper. Because of its high tin content, it is quite expensive and often difficult to obtain. It was used a great deal during early colonial days but is not nearly so popular now as a project choice. Some of the early pewter contained lead, which

made it poisonous to use with acid foods. It is very soft and easy to work cold but is difficult to solder because of its low melting point.

6. *Aluminum* is a bluish-white lustrous metal and is one of the most important nonferrous metals. The common aluminum for art metalwork and cold forming is called 2S and is commercially pure, 3S has a little manganese, and 52S contains a little magnesium and chromium. These are the only kinds that should be used for art metalwork. Alloys that can be heat-treated are 24S, 61S, and 75S, none of which is suitable for projects. For casting aluminum, 43 or 112 alloy is satisfactory. The 2S and 3S aluminum have very fine cold-working characteristics but are difficult to soft-solder. The annealing of these is also difficult since it is easy to overheat and melt thin sheet aluminum.

7. *Sterling silver* is used in the better jewelry and tableware and has a warm silver luster. To be marked "sterling," the article must contain at least 0.925 part of silver with 0.075 part of copper and other alloying elements to give it hardness. Pure silver is too soft. Sterling silver, while not so ductile as copper, can be formed and shaped well. It is very good for chasing, etching, and all other surface decorations, and it hard-solders well.

The Ferrous Metals

Steels are composed primarily of iron with small amounts of carbon and other elements added to produce alloys with the desired qualities. Carbon is such an important element in all steels that they are classified by the amount of carbon they contain. The following vary from the least to the most carbon: wrought iron, low-carbon steel, medium-carbon steel, high-carbon steel, and cast iron. It has been found that steel with a carbon content of 75 points (100 points equal 1 per cent) is a good quality of carbon steel for heat-treating; it is called *high-carbon steel*. This would be used for making such projects as center punches, knives, cold chisels, and similar articles that must be heat-treated. Most other steels used for bench-metal, wrought-iron, and sheet-metal projects are low-carbon steels. Alloy steels are widely used in modern industry and contain small amounts of the other metals. For example, manganese is added to increase wear resistance, nickel for strength and toughness, chromium for hardness and strength, tungsten for good cutting edges, and molybdenum for shock resistance.

It would be impossible to identify steels by just looking at them. There are three methods of identification:

1. *The number system.* The American Iron and Steel Institute (A.I.S.I.) or the Society of Automotive Engineers (S.A.E.) numbering system consists of four numbers for each kind of steel. The first number tells the kind of metal; the second, the approximate percentage of alloying metal; and the last two numbers, the approximate points of carbon. For example, 2335 steel means: 2, that it is a nickel steel; 3, that it contains about 3 per cent nickel; and 35, that it contains 35 points of carbon. Tables showing the complete numbering system are given in any machinist handbook.

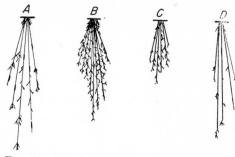

Fig. 6-2. How to identify the metal by the spark: (*A*) low-carbon steel, (*B*) high-carbon steel, (*C*) cast iron, and (*D*) stainless steel.

2. *The color painted on it.* All companies have an individual color code that they paint on the ends of the bars of steel. Each color indicates a particular kind of steel. For example, plain red may be a certain kind of high-carbon steel.

3. *Spark test.* When steel is ground, sparks are given off, and the steel can be approximately identified by the appearance of the spark (Fig. 6-2).

All ferrous metals in plate and sheet form are measured by the United States Standard (U.S.S.) gauge. (See Table 6-1.) You will probably use some of the following common ferrous metals:

1. *Wrought iron* is almost pure iron with most of the carbon removed. It is the choice for a great deal of ornamental ironwork, although it is not frequently found in the school shop because of its high cost. It forges well, can easily be bent hot or cold, and can be welded.

2. *Low-carbon steel,* often called *mild steel,* contains about 10 to 30 points of carbon. It is available in all forms as black iron sheet, band iron, bars and rods and is used for most bench-metal or

ornamental ironwork. It is easily worked but requires slightly higher temperatures for forging than wrought iron. It will not heat-treat except by casehardening.

3. *High-carbon steel,* called *tool steel,* contains about 50 to 150 points of carbon. The best for school shops contains 75 to 85 points of carbon and is used for making small tools or for any project that must be hardened and tempered.

4. *Galvanized, or galvannealed, sheet* is a mild steel coated with zinc to protect it from rusting.

5. *Tin plate* is mild steel coated with tin. It is measured by the United States Standard gauge or by a trade symbol: ICL, IC, IX, IXX to IXXXXXX. The higher the number of X's, the thicker the tin plate.

Discussion Topics

1. What is the difference between a metal and an alloy?
2. Name the common ferrous metals. Nonferrous metals.
3. How does hardness affect a metal?

4. Define "brittleness" and tell how it differs from "hardness."
5. What quality makes metals capable of being bent and stretched?
6. What quality do metals possess that makes them capable of being drawn into wire?
7. Describe fusibility and corrosiveness.
8. Why are some metals called "ferrous" and others "nonferrous"?
9. How is the sheet stock of each measured?
10. Describe the following as to color, content, and workability: copper, brass, bronze, nickel silver, pewter, aluminum, and sterling silver. What is this group called?
11. Is steel ferrous or nonferrous? How does the carbon content affect steel? Explain.
12. How can you tell one steel from another?
13. Name the ferrous metals you will be using in the shop.

Unit 7. Planning a Project

When the drawing for the project is complete, a great deal of planning must be done before construction can begin. In industry these plans are called *shop orders, routing orders,* or *specifications.* It is the wise person who plans his work before building, for this is the only way to avoid mistakes. It is good practice to make out a plan sheet like the one in Fig. 7-1, which has three major parts: the bill of materials, equipment and tools to be used, and procedure or steps for making the project.

Making a Bill of Materials

It is important to specify exactly what items are needed to build the project. Each item should be written accurately and clearly enough so that the list could be sent to a metal supply house and the proper items secured in return. The bill of materials includes the number of pieces, size of the piece, a description of it, the cost per unit, and the total cost.

Table 7-1 includes a list of the common materials and a description of how to order them. A stock list or handbook of materials can be secured from almost any company that manufactures and sells metal supplies.

Equipment and Tools

All the equipment and tools that you need should be listed. This will save time and energy when the project is made, since everything can be assembled before the work is started.

Procedure or Steps

The best way to make a plan of procedure is to break up the finished article into the parts that go into it and then to think through what you must do to make each part. As a final step, think through the plans that are included in assembling and finishing the article. A typical plan sheet is shown for making book ends (Fig. 7–2, page 25).

Name_____ Grade_____

Project_____ Date started_____

                                         Date completed_____

BILL OF MATERIALS:

No. of pieces	Size			Name of part	Material	Unit cost	Total cost
	T	W	L				

EQUIPMENT AND TOOLS:

PROCEDURE OR STEPS:
   1. Cut out the stock.

   2. Make Part 1.
      a.
      b.
      c.
      d.
      e.
      Etc.
   3. Make Part 2.
      a.
      b.
      c.
      Etc.
   4. Make Part 3.
      Etc.
   5. Assemble.

   6. Finish.

Fig. 7-1. Use a form like this one when planning your project. Follow the plan as you build it.

TABLE 7-1. COMMON MATERIALS USED IN METALWORK

Material	Common sizes (suggested sizes for average projects)	How sold (common)	Characteristics
A. Sheet Stock			
Galvanized iron (steel)....	U.S.S. gauge No. 28 to 26 for light projects U.S.S. gauge No. 22 to 20 for heavier projects	24″ × 96″ by sheet or bundles	Mild steel with zinc coating
Galvannealed iron (steel)..	Same as above	Same as above	Mild steel with zinc coating that is part of the sheet
Tin plate..............	U.S.S. gauge No. 30 or 28 (IC or IX) for light items	20″ × 28″ by sheet or by package of 56 or 112 sheets	Mild steel with tin coating cold-rolled to thickness
Black iron (steel; annealed)	U.S.S. gauge No. 26 to 22 for lighter projects U.S.S. gauge No. 20 to 18 for heavier projects	24″ × 96″ by sheet or bundle	Mild steel with black iron oxide coating
Aluminum (2S or 3S; soft temper)	B&S gauge 18 or 0.040 for light projects B&S gauge 14 or 0.064 for heavier projects	24″ × 72″ by sheet or by lineal foot on rolls	Commercially pure metal
Copper (soft)...........	16 oz. for light work 24 oz. for medium work 32 oz. for heavy work	24″ × 96″ by sheet	Pure metal
Brass (soft).............	B&S gauge 18 for average work	24″ × 76″ by sheet or by lineal foot on rolls	Copper and zinc
Nickel silver (german silver)	B&S gauge 18 and 12	6″ or 12″ by lineal foot	65% copper, 17% zinc, and 18% nickel
B. Mild Steel Shapes			
Band (or strap).........	$\frac{1}{8}″ \times \frac{1}{2}″$, $\frac{1}{8}″ \times \frac{3}{4}″$, $\frac{1}{8}″ \times 1″$ for bench or wrought-iron projects	16′ lengths per lb. or ft.	S.A.E. 1020 hot-rolled mild steel with oxide coating
Rounds (shafting).......	$\frac{1}{2}″$, $\frac{3}{4}″$, 1″ for machine or small tool parts not requiring heat-treating and for forging	12′ or 16′ lengths per lb. or ft.	S.A.E. 1020 hot-rolled with oxide coating or cold-rolled
Squares (bar)...........	$\frac{1}{2}″ \times \frac{1}{2}″$, $\frac{3}{4}″ \times \frac{3}{4}″$, 1″ × 1″, $1\frac{1}{2}″ \times 1\frac{1}{2}″$ for small tools that are to be casehardened or for wrought-iron projects	12′ or 16′ lengths per lb. or ft.	S.A.E. 1020 hot-rolled with oxide coating or cold-rolled
Flats.................	$\frac{1}{2}″ \times 1\frac{1}{4}″$, $\frac{1}{2}″ \times 2″$ for small tools	12′ lengths	S.A.E. 1020 hot-rolled

23

TABLE 7-1. COMMON MATERIALS USED IN METALWORK. (*Continued*)

Material	Common sizes (suggested sizes for average projects)	How sold (common)	Characteristics
Angle..............	$1\frac{1}{2}'' \times 1\frac{1}{2}'' \times \frac{1}{8}''$, $2'' \times 2'' \times \frac{3}{16}''$ for bench legs and structure	12' or 16' lengths per lb. or ft.	S.A.E. 1020 hot-rolled
C. Tool Steel Shapes			
Flats..............	$\frac{1}{8}'' \times 1\frac{1}{2}''$ for knives	12' or 14' lengths by lb.	S.A.E. 1075 annealed; can be hardened and tempered
Rounds..............	$\frac{1}{2}''$ or $\frac{9}{16}''$ or $\frac{5}{8}''$ for punches	12' or 14' lengths by lb.	S.A.E. 1075 annealed; can be hardened and tempered
Hexagon..............	$\frac{1}{2}''$ or $\frac{3}{4}''$ for chisels or punches	12' or 14' lengths by lb.	S.A.E. 1075 annealed; can be hardened and tempered
Octagon..............	$\frac{3}{8}''$, $\frac{1}{2}''$, $\frac{5}{8}''$, $\frac{3}{4}''$ for chisels or punches	12' or 14' lengths by lb.	S.A.E. 1075 annealed; can be hardened and tempered
Drill rod..............	Various diameters ($\frac{1}{8}''$, $\frac{3}{16}''$, $\frac{1}{4}''$, $\frac{3}{8}''$) for small tools	3' lengths	S.A.E. 1075 annealed; can be hardened and tempered
D. Other Items			
Pipe..............	$\frac{1}{8}''$ in black iron, brass, and copper, for electric lamps	12' lengths by lb. or ft.	S.A.E. 1020 black iron, copper, brass
Rivets..............	$\frac{1}{8}'' \times 1$, $\frac{3}{16}'' \times 1''$ round head & flat, black (soft) iron for bench metal or wrought iron	By lb.	
	$\frac{1}{8}'' \times 1''$ aluminum, copper, & brass round head	By lb.	
	1 & 2 lb. black iron and tinned tinner's rivets	By box	
Machine screws and nuts..	6-32-1''–$1\frac{1}{2}''$ 8-32-1''–$1\frac{1}{2}''$ steel, round or flat head and brass round head for small machine assembly	By gross	
Wire..............	U.S.S. gauge Nos. 10, 12, 14, 18 black soft annealed wire or coppered bessemer wire or soft galvanized wire, for sheet metal work	By weight of coil	
Foundry metal..............	Aluminum casting alloy No. 43 or 112	By lb.	
	Die cast metal	By lb.	

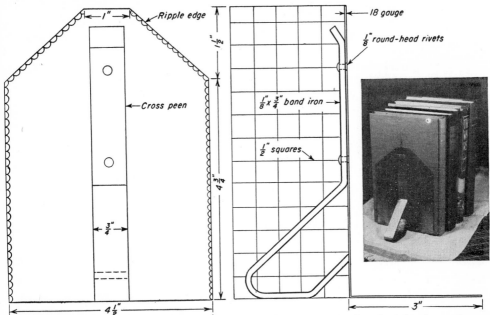

Fig. 7-2. A drawing and photograph of the finished book ends described in the project-planning sheet.

BOOK ENDS

BILL OF MATERIALS

2 pieces, 18 gauge, $4\frac{1}{2}'' \times 9\frac{1}{4}''$, body, black iron

2 pieces $\frac{1}{8}'' \times \frac{3}{4}'' \times 9\frac{1}{2}''$, supports, band iron

4 $\frac{1}{8}''$ round-head rivets, black iron

EQUIPMENT AND TOOLS

Hacksaw, rule, scriber, prick punch, center punch, $\frac{1}{8}''$ drill, bench shears or snips, drill press, grinder, rivet set, file, abrasive cloth, countersink, ball peen hammer, cross peen hammer.

PROCEDURE

1. Cut all pieces to the exact size.
2. Make the body of the book ends.
   a. Lay out the design on the book ends.
   b. Cut the design with snips or bench shears.
   c. File the edges smooth.
   d. Remove all the black iron oxide with abrasive cloth.
   e. Peen the edges with a ball-peen hammer.
   f. Mark in 3 inches from the bottom and bend a right angle.
3. Make the supports.
   a. Remove all the black iron oxide with abrasive cloth.
   b. Peen the surface with a cross-peen hammer.
   c. Peen one end with a ball-peen hammer.
   d. Locate and bend at the proper positions. Check each bend on a full-size layout.
   e. Grind the lower end of the support at an angle until it fits against the body.
   f. Locate the position of the rivet holes and drill with a $\frac{1}{8}$-inch drill.
4. Assemble the book ends.
   a. Hold the support in proper position against the body and mark the location of one of the holes.
   b. Center punch and drill this hole with a $\frac{1}{8}$-inch drill.

c. Countersink the back side of the body.

d. Insert the first rivet in the hole, and cut off the rivet so that only a small amount comes through.

e. Hold the head of the rivet over a rivet set and flatten the shank.

f. Drill and countersink the second hole and repeat the riveting.

5. Apply two coats of clear lacquer. Glue a piece of felt to the bottom.

Discussion Topics

1. Why must you plan a project before starting to build it?

2. Make out the bill of materials for a simple project.

3. List the tools and equipment needed for this project.

4. Make out the plan of procedure.

Unit 8. Measuring and Marking Out Stock

Measuring and marking out stock is the first step in the construction of any project. It is important to learn to use the common layout tools correctly (Fig. 8-1).

Layout Tools

Steel rule. The 6- and 12-inch steel rules are graduated into inches and fractions of an inch: halves, quarters, eighths, sixteenths, thirty-seconds, and sixty-fourths (Fig. 8-2). A good steel rule is made with the inches divided into at least sixteenths on one edge and thirty-seconds on the other. When measuring or marking out distances, it must be held on edge to be accurate (Fig. 8-3). To measure lengths if the end is worn, the measurement should start with the inch mark. Fractions of an inch have their decimal

Fig. 8-1. The layout tools and materials needed for most work. From left to right they are: layout fluid, metal with layout fluid applied, 12-inch steel rule, scriber, dividers, combination set, prick punch, center punch, and ball-peen hammer.

TABLE 8-1. DECIMAL EQUIVALENTS

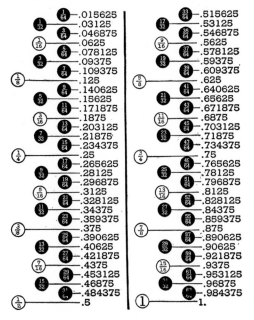

	1/64 —.015625		33/64—.515625
1/32	.03125	17/32	.53125
	3/64 .046875		35/64 .546875
1/16	.0625	9/16	.5625
	5/64 .078125		37/64 .578125
3/32	.09375	19/32	.59375
	7/64 .109375		39/64 .609375
1/8	.125	5/8	.625
	9/64 .140625		41/64 .640625
5/32	.15625	21/32	.65625
	11/64 .171875		43/64 .671875
3/16	.1875	11/16	.6875
	13/64 .203125		45/64 .703125
7/32	.21875	23/32	.71875
	15/64 .234375		47/64 .734375
1/4	.25	3/4	.75
	17/64 .265625		49/64 .765625
9/32	.28125	25/32	.78125
	19/64 .296875		51/64 .796875
5/16	.3125	13/16	.8125
	21/64 .328125		53/64 .828125
11/32	.34375	27/32	.84375
	23/64 .359375		55/64 .859375
3/8	.375	7/8	.875
	25/64 .390625		57/64 .890625
13/32	.40625	29/32	.90625
	27/64 .421875		59/64 .921875
7/16	.4375	15/16	.9375
	29/64 .453125		61/64 .953125
15/32	.46875	31/32	.96875
	31/64 .484375		63/64 .984375
1/2	.5	1	1.

Fig. 8-2. The divisions on a steel rule. Frequently, one side of the rule will be divided into eighths and sixteenths and the other side into thirty-seconds and sixty-fourths.

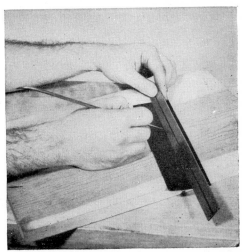

Fig. 8-3. Measuring the length of stock. The rule is held on edge with the inch mark over the end of stock, and a scriber is used to mark accurately the length desired.

equivalents, which are shown in Table 8-1.

Be sure that you can read a rule. It is surprising how few people can find specific measurements on a rule such as $\frac{7}{16}$ or $\frac{13}{32}$. More errors are made through incorrect layout than in any other step in metalworking.

Circumference rule. For sheet-metal layout a steel 36-inch circumference rule is very useful (Fig. 8-4). It gets its name from the fact that along one edge there is a regular rule divided into sixteenths while along the other edge there is a scale which shows the circumference for that diameter. For example, if you want to lay out a piece of sheet metal to roll into a 4-inch diameter cylinder, find the length required by locating the 4-inch mark on the rule and looking across to the mark on the scale, which would be $12\frac{9}{16}$ inches. A *steel square* is also a good

Fig. 8-4. A circumference rule is a useful tool in sheet-metal work, since it will give the circumference needed when the diameter is known.

layout tool for large sheet-stock layout (Fig. 8-5).

Steel tape. For many longer measurements, a steel tape (Fig. 8-6) is convenient, since it can be bent around circular objects and the measurements can be made on the inside or outside of openings. It is particularly helpful because of a little hook on the end which holds it in place for taking long measurements.

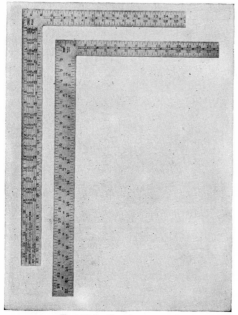

FIG. 8-5. Steel squares.

one head is placed on the blade at one time. The square head is used like a try square to lay out 90-degree angles, to check the squareness of two surfaces, and in many other ways. One side of the head makes a 45-degree angle with the blade. The center head is used primarily to locate the center on the end of round stock. This is done in preparing stock to be turned in a lathe. The protractor head can be adjusted to lay out any angle from 0 to 180 degrees (Fig. 8-7).

Scriber. The scriber is a metalworker's pencil and is a long, thin piece of steel with a sharp point on one end. A double-pointed scriber has a straight point on one end, while the other is bent to an angle of 90 degrees to reach out-of-the-way places. The point of the scriber should always be held closely against the rule (Fig. 8-8).

Combination set. The combination set is a layout device that has many uses. It consists of a 12-inch steel rule or blade with three different heads: the square head, the center head, and the protractor head. The blade has a groove cut down one side of it, along its length, to hold the head firmly in place. Only

Prick punch. The prick punch is made from a piece of hardened steel and has a point ground at an angle of 30 degrees (Fig. 8-9). It is used only for layout work, for example, transferring a layout from a paper to metal, making a small indentation when laying out circles with

FIG. 8-6. A steel tape is especially useful when measuring around curved sections, such as on this model boat.

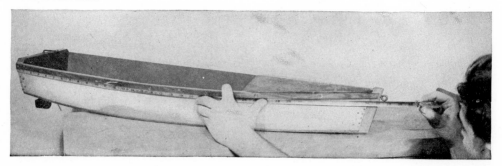

(a)

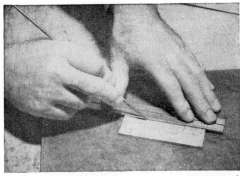

Fig. 8-8. Tilt the point of the scriber in toward the corner formed between the rule and the metal.

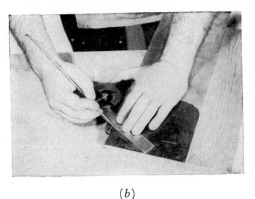

(b)

Center Punch   Prick Punch

90°   30°

Fig. 8-9. A center punch is ground to an angle of 90 degress. The prick punch is ground to an angle of 30 degrees.

Fig. 8-7. (a) Using a scriber and the square head of a combination set to mark a line across stock. (b) Using the protractor head to lay out an angle. (c) Common uses for the square and center head.

(c)

dividers, and locating the center of holes to be drilled (Fig. 8-10).

Center punch. The center punch is very similar to the prick punch except that the point is ground at an angle of 90 degrees. It is used to enlarge a hole made by the prick punch when the hole is to be drilled (Fig. 8-10).

Hammer. The hammer most commonly used is called the *ball-peen ham-*

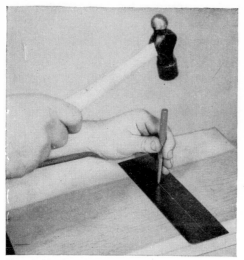

Fig. 8-10. A prick punch is used to mark the location. Before drilling, this punch mark should be enlarged with the center punch.

mer and is made in various sizes, depending upon the weight of the head, from 4 ounces to 3 pounds. It is used for striking punches, chisels, and rivet sets

and for riveting, peening, and bending metal. Two hammers similar to it are the *cross-peen* and *straight peen* (Fig. 8-11). Although the hammer is a very common tool, it is often used incorrectly. Grasp it toward the end of the handle, not close to the head. As you pound, always watch the place where you want the hammer to strike, never the hammer head.

Dividers. Dividers consist of two pointed steel legs with sharpened points that can be adjusted to any width of opening. They are used for scribing arcs and circles, for measuring irregular shapes such as scrolls, and for laying out equal distances along an arc or circle. To be effective, the points of the dividers must be kept sharp. To set the dividers, place one leg over the inch mark of a rule, and open the thumb nut until the other leg spans the correct

Fig. 8-11. Three kinds of peen hammers.

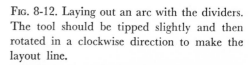

Ball peen

Eye

Wedges

Handle

Neck

Cheek

Poll

Face

Straight peen

Cross peen

Fig. 8-12. Laying out an arc with the dividers. The tool should be tipped slightly and then rotated in a clockwise direction to make the layout line.

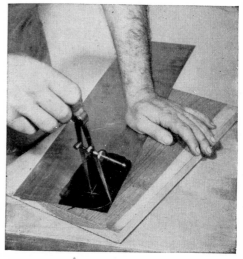

distance. When scribing an arc or circle, grasp the dividers by the knurled handle with one leg in the prick-punch mark, and then twirl the dividers as you would a compass (Fig. 8-12).

MEASURING AND MARKING OUT

To measure the thickness of a piece of metal, hold the rule on edge with one edge of the metal on the inch mark. The mark above the other edge will indicate the thickness. Measure the width in the same manner.

MEASURING AND MARKING OUT THE LENGTH OF BAND IRON, RODS, AND BARS

Hold the rule on edge with one end over one end of the stock. With the scriber carefully mark the correct length of stock needed (Fig. 8-3). If it is rectangular in shape, use the square head of a combination square to mark a line indicating where the stock is to be cut off (Fig. 8-7a).

MARKING STOCK TO BE CUT FROM SHEET

Make sure that an edge and an end are square with one another. Hold a rule over the end of the stock, and mark out a point that indicates the length of stock to be cut. Move the rule over and mark out another point for the length. Join these two points with a scribed line. Now mark several points to indicate the width, lay a straight edge along these points, and scribe a line (Fig. 8-13).

FIG. 8-13. When laying out on a flat sheet, mark several points to indicate the length or width of stock needed. Then hold a rule over these points and scribe a line.

Discussion Topics

1. Describe the steel rule.
2. Find the following measurements on a steel rule and make a sketch pointing them out: $\frac{3}{4}, \frac{5}{8}, \frac{9}{16}, \ 2\frac{1}{.}$
3. How is a circumference rule used?
4. In what way is a steel tape useful?
5. What are the three heads of a combination set used for?
6. How should the scriber be held when scribing lines on metal?
7. For what steps in layout work is the prick punch used?
8. How can the prick-punch mark be enlarged?
9. What kind of hammers will you need? How do you hold a hammer?
10. Describe the dividers. Why must the points be kept sharp?
11. What tools are needed for measuring and marking out stock? Tell how you would proceed.
12. How are band iron, rods, and bars measured and marked out?
13. Tell how to mark out a piece that is to be cut from a large sheet.

Unit 9. Making a Simple Layout

When stock has been cut to approximate size, the layout must be made. The layout is an exact duplication of the drawing on the metal surface. In order to obtain a good layout, it is necessary to know how to read the print, how to use layout tools correctly, and how to make an accurate layout. Often the layout is made on a piece of metal that has been cut slightly larger than the finished size.

Enlarging a Pattern

Before a layout can be made, the pattern must often be enlarged to full size. This is especially true of complicated and unusual designs found on art metal projects. The procedure is relatively simple.

1. Lay out squares on the original drawing. Most patterns will already be laid out on squared paper, but if not, cover the drawing with squares of a fractional-inch size, depending on the scale to which the drawing has been made. Then, when you lay out inch squares for the full-size pattern, it will be enlarged correctly. For example, if the drawing is one-fourth full size, lay out $\frac{1}{4}$-inch squares on the original drawing.

2. Lay out inch squares on a large piece of wrapping paper. Letter across the bottom and number up the left side, as shown in Fig. 9-1, on both the original drawing and on the enlarged pattern. Locate a position on the original drawing and transfer it to the corresponding position on the enlarged pattern. Do this until you have located enough points to draw the pattern layout full size. Connect these points with a pencil, using a straight edge for the straight lines and

a French curve or bent wire for the curved lines. If the design is symmetrical, only half of the pattern requires development.

Layout Fluids

The layout on the metal will be of no value if you cannot see it. Therefore, the metal surface should be covered with some kind of layout fluid.

1. *Bluing fluid* is a bluish-purple and can be painted on the metal surface like ink. When it dries, scribed lines show up clearly.

2. *Show-card white* can be painted on many metal surfaces, especially if the design or pattern is to be transferred by the carbon-paper method.

3. *Zinc chromate primer,* which is a material applied to aluminum to prevent corrosion, also acts as a very good layout fluid.

4. *Copper sulfate* can be used successfully on iron and steel, and when it is painted on a clear surface, it turns blue.

Making Layout Directly on Metal

A layout will vary with each different project so that only general suggestions can be made. Before starting, be sure that you have the right size and kind of metal (Fig. 9-2).

1. Cut or file one edge and end at right angles to each other. Use this edge and end as reference lines and make all measurements from these two edges.

2. Apply some kind of layout fluid.

3. Lay out all straight lines to indicate the widths and lengths of the various parts.

32

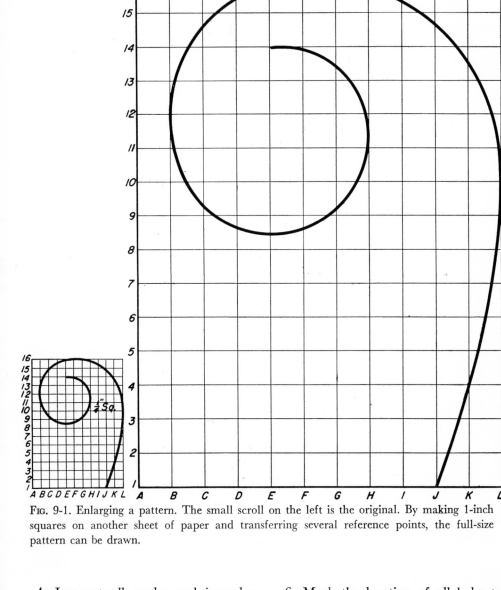

FIG. 9-1. Enlarging a pattern. The small scroll on the left is the original. By making 1-inch squares on another sheet of paper and transferring several reference points, the full-size pattern can be drawn.

4. Lay out all angles and irregular lines.

5. Lay out all arcs.

6. Mark the location of all holes to be drilled.

7. Lay out all internal lines.

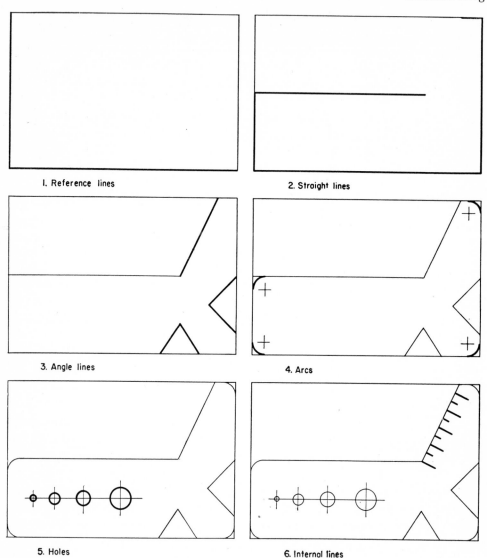

FIG. 9-2. Steps in laying out a combination gauge.

TRANSFERRING A DESIGN

If the design is irregular or complicated, there are several simple methods of transferring it.

1. Draw the design on thin paper and glue this to the metal surface with household cement or tape (Fig. 9-3).

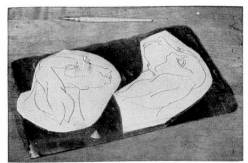

Fig. 9-3. The layout for this tooling project was done by attaching the design to the metal with transparent tape.

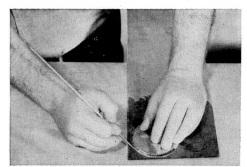

Fig. 9-5. The template is the simplest way of transferring a design, especially when many identical parts must be laid out.

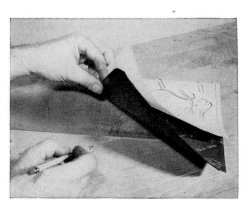

Fig. 9-4. The carbon-paper method. This is very useful when the metal is to be cut or pierced with a saw.

2. Apply a coat of show-card white, and then transfer the design to the metal by the carbon-paper method. Fasten a piece of carbon paper and then the design to the metal, clipping these in place. With a pencil or blunt instrument outline the design (Fig. 9-4).

3. If many articles of the same shape are to be made, a template of plywood or sheet metal can be cut. This is held on the metal and the pattern traced with a scriber (Fig. 9-5).

Discussion Topics

1. What is a "layout"?
2. Find a pattern in a book or magazine that is one-eighth or one-fourth full size, and enlarge it to full size on a large sheet of paper.
3. What are some materials that can be painted on metal to make layout markings show?
4. Is it possible to make a layout directly on metal?
5. There are several ways to transfer a design. What are they?

Section II. BENCH METAL AND WROUGHT IRON

Unit 10. Introduction to Bench Metal

Your first experience in the metal shop will probably be in bench metal, because this is fundamental to all other metalwork (Fig. 10-1). It is sometimes called *hand tools, elementary machine shop, bench work, cold-metal work,* or *metal fitting.* You will learn to use hand tools for cutting, forming, drilling, shaping, threading, and riveting mild steel in the forms of bands, rods, squares, and black iron sheet. Ornamental ironwork, or wrought iron, especially that done with cold metals, is also a part of bench metal and involves the same operations plus a few additional ones such as bending curves and scrolls and twisting metal. The projects are sometimes called *wrought-iron projects,* even though, in most cases, the material used is not actually wrought iron, which is too expensive (Fig. 10-2).

All metalsmiths and many mechanics must master the use of hand tools; this is often more difficult than operating some machines. For example, a tool-and diemaker must possess exceptional hand skills to finish the expensive dies used in the production of metal parts. He has a more skilled job than a machinist and is, therefore, better paid. There are hundreds of thousands of people who work as auto mechanics, assemblers, and machine repairmen who must know how to handle bench-metal tools. Even the professions of medicine and dentistry depend on the skillful use of precision tools.

Regardless of how you will earn a living, however, learning to use these hand tools is a fine accomplishment and will enable you to do such things as to repair a bicycle or automobile, to put a new lock in a door, or to do any of the small maintenance jobs in the shop and home. These hand skills will also enable you to take apart, to adjust, and to repair such electrical and mechanical appliances as vacuum cleaners, oil burners, motor scooters, and outboard motors.

Bench metal may also become a very satisfying hobby. There are many things that can be made of wrought iron, such as post lamps, foot scrapers, house num-

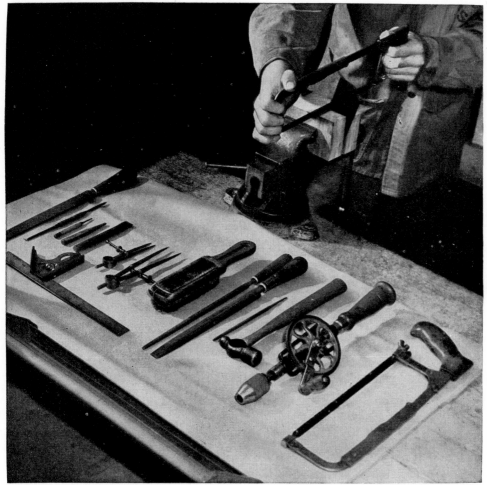

FIG. 10-1. A metalworker must master all kinds of hand tools. You, too, will find these skills useful in any kind of work.

Discussion Topics

bers, and book ends. In many sections of the country, hobbyists have formed guilds or clubs that sell their products in roadside stands, at summer resorts, and in gift shops and have become well known through national magazine advertising.

1. What sort of work will you be doing in bench metal?

2. In which occupations is bench metal used?

3. What type of things can be made in bench metal? Would it make a good hobby?

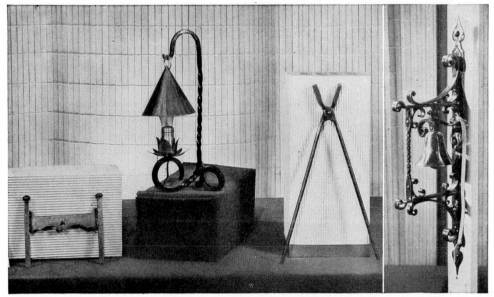

Fɪɢ. 10-2. These attractive metal projects are typical of the ones made in wrought iron. They were made in a school shop and have won national industrial arts awards.

Unit 11. Cutting Heavy Stock

There are several ways to cut band or strap iron and heavy black iron sheet. Common tools are the hack saw, cold chisel, bench shears, and power saw.

Hack Saws and Blades

The U-shaped frame of a hack saw is made either solid for one size blade or adjustable for various lengths of blades (Fig. 11-1). The correct selection of blades is important, so consider the following:

1. Blades are made of tool, high-speed, or tungsten steel. The most common lengths are the 10 and 12 inches.

2. The number of teeth per inch varies with the purpose of the blade: from 12 to 14 teeth per inch for cutting soft stock such as copper, brass, or aluminum to 32 teeth per inch for cutting thin metal tubing or thin sheet stock. For most work select a 10- or 12-inch high-speed steel blade with 18 teeth per inch. This general rule should be followed: choose a fine blade for thin stock so that at least three teeth are in contact with the metal at all times.

3. Teeth are bent to the right and left (called *set*) so that they will cut a *kerf* that is slightly wider than the blade itself to prevent binding. The *regular alternate set*, which has teeth bent alternately to left and right, is used for all ordinary work. A *wave-set* blade for cutting thin

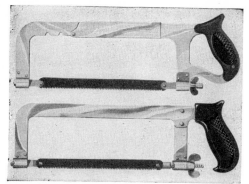

FIG. 11-1. Hack saws. Top, an adjustable-type hack-saw frame that can be used with blades of different lengths. Bottom, a solid-type frame that is used with single-length blades.

CUTTING WITH A HACK SAW

1. Select the correct blade and insert it in the frame with the teeth pointing away from the handle (Fig. 11-2). Tighten the wing nut or handle until the blade is taut enough to ring clear when struck.

2. Fasten the stock in a vise with the layout line extending just beyond the edge of the vise jaws. If the jaws are knurled, cover them with soft aluminum or copper to protect the work (Fig.11-3). Place wide pieces in the vise with the flat surface horizontal. Sandwich thin stock between two scrap pieces of wood. Place thin pipe or tubing in a wooden jig (Fig. 11-4).

3. Hold your left thumb over the layout line as a guide for the blade. Start the kerf by taking a few short strokes, operating the saw with your right hand only.

4. When the cut has been started, grasp the end of the hack saw in your left hand as shown in Fig. 11-5. Correct

pipe or tubing has the teeth bent alternately to right and left in groups of five or six.

4. Blades are heat-treated to make them either hard or flexible. The flexible blade is better because it does not break so easily.

FIG. 11-2. The steps in installing a blade in a frame.

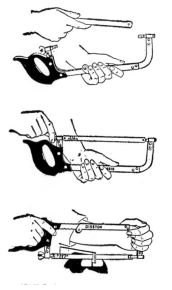

FIG. 11-3. Soft jaws of aluminum, copper, or brass will protect the metal when it is clamped in a vise.

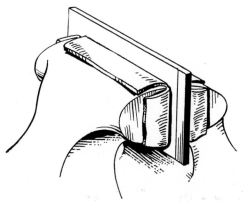

Holding Work in Vise

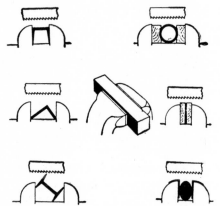

FIG. 11-4. The ways in which stock should be held in a vise for cutting with a hack saw.

cutting action is secured by applying pressure on the forward stroke, releasing pressure at the end of the stroke, and returning to the starting position. Watch the operation of an automatic hack saw if one is available. Maintain a uniform speed of about one forward stroke per second, using the entire length of the blade. Most beginners take short, jabbing strokes and apply equal pressure on both forward and return strokes, with poor results.

FIG. 11-5. The proper method of holding the hack saw. Use the total length of the blade.

5. To make the last few cuts, hold the piece in your left hand and operate the saw with the right hand only.

6. To make a long cut on sheet stock, turn the blade at right angles to the frame after you have cut as deeply as you can with the blade in the regular position.

7. Check your work. Did you twist or break the blade or break any of its teeth? Is the cut crooked? Does it follow the layout line?

COLD CHISELS

Cold chisels of hardened tool or alloy steel are used to cut and shear metal. Figure 11-6 shows some of the common

FIG. 11-6. The four common kinds of cold chisels: (*a*) the flat, for ordinary cutting and shearing, should be ground to an angle of 60 degrees; (*b*) the diamond point for cleaning out a sharp corner or finishing a square opening; (*c*) the cape for making grooves; and (*d*) the roundnose for cutting circular depressions.

(*a*)

(*b*)

(*c*)

(*d*)

types. Flat cold chisels in widths from $\frac{1}{8}$ to $\frac{3}{4}$ inch are most common.

SHARPENING A CHISEL

A dull chisel is a poor cutting tool and a very dangerous one. Grind off the mushroom head that has formed, and then sharpen the cutting edge to a 60- to 65-degree included angle for ordinary work. The edge can be straight across or slightly curved.

CUTTING OVER A FLAT PLATE

This kind of cutting is done primarily on irregular lines, since in straight-line cutting other methods are simpler.

1. Place the stock over a flat plate. *Never use the surface of an anvil or a surface plate from the machine shop.*
2. Hold the chisel firmly in your left hand, striking a solid blow with a ball-peen hammer.

3. Follow the layout line, first making small indentations over the entire pattern (Fig. 11-7).

4. Go back over the line, striking the chisel with firmer blows to cut through the metal. If necessary, turn the stock over and cut from the opposite side.

SHEARING IN A VISE

1. Clamp the stock with the layout line just above the vise jaws.
2. Hold the chisel at an angle of about 30 degrees to the surface of the jaws.
3. Start at one end of the work, striking the chisel with firm blows to shear the metal (Fig. 11-8). Do not hold the head of the chisel too high or you will cut into the vise jaws.

CUTTING AN INTERNAL OPENING

First drill a series of small holes just inside the waste material, and then cut out the opening with a chisel (Fig. 11-9).

FIG. 11-7. The way a chisel should be held when cutting metal over a flat plate. The chisel may be held at a slight angle to the work when cutting the first impression.

FIG. 11-8. Shearing metal in a vise. Keep the chisel at the proper angle in order not to cut into the vise jaws or tear the metal.

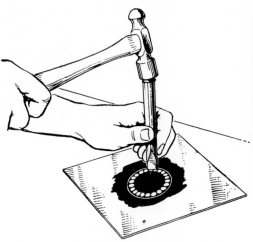

Fig. 11-11. Using a throatless bench shears. Make sure that the metal is inserted as far into the shear as is possible. Keep your fingers away from the sharp cutting edges.

Fig. 11-9. Cutting out an internal opening. Note that a series of holes has been drilled just inside the waste stock. This makes it easy to cut out the opening with a chisel. Finish the edge by filing.

BENCH SHEARS

There are two kinds of bench shears. The *bench lever shears* with straight blades is used for cutting band or strap iron and black iron sheet to size. To operate, open the blades, insert the metal with the layout line directly over the

shearing edge, and then carefully lower the handle to cut the stock (Fig. 11-10). The *throatless bench shears* with curved blades is used to make curved or irregular cuts on sheet stock as well as straight cuts. When cutting an irregular shape, constantly move the stock as you cut, following the layout line (Fig. 11-11).

POWER SAWING

A power saw will greatly reduce the time needed for cutting out project parts.

Fig. 11-10. A regular-type bench shears.

Fig. 11-12. A regular power hack saw that takes blades similar to the hand hack saw.

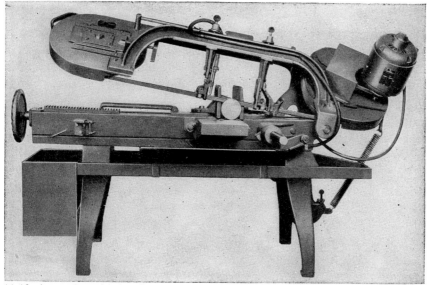

Fig. 11-13. A metal-cutting band saw with a continuous blade such as is used in a wood band saw. When starting the cut, allow the blade to come down slowly on the work.

Discussion Topics

There are two kinds: the regular *power hack saw* and the *metal-cutting power band saw* (Figs. 11-12 and 11-13). Both operate in the same way. Clamp the stock in the vise with the layout line directly under the blade. Lower the blade slowly to cutting position. The actual cutting is automatic. Both machines are equipped with stops that can be set for cutting duplicate parts. *Never use these machines until they have been demonstrated.*

1. Name the tools used for cutting heavy stock.
2. How should the blade be installed in the hack-saw frame?
3. How is a chisel sharpened?
4. There are several ways of doing heavy cutting with a chisel. Tell how to cut over a flat plate, how to shear in a vise, and how to cut an internal opening.
5. What power saws will cut heavy stock?

Unit 12. Drilling Holes

Drills and drilling devices are often used to drill holes in tapping, to assemble with rivets, and to make all types of cut-out designs. Remember, there will be only one set of drills of each type in the shop, and these are easily broken or ruined if improperly used. It is very important to study drills and the proper method of drilling.

DRILLS

The *twist drill* is made of either carbon or high-speed steel. The *carbon-steel drill* is suitable for most types of metalworking, but the *high-speed steel drill,* identified by "HS" between the shank and the body, is better for harder steels and has the advantage of not dulling rapidly.

The parts of a drill are shown in Fig. 12-1*a*. Study these to learn their location and use.

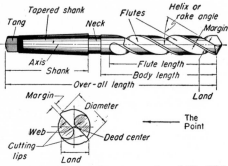

FIG. 12-1*a*. The major parts of a drill. This drill has a tapered shank.

SHANKS

The *straight shank* is most common especially on drills of ½ inch or smaller. The *bitstock shank* is used with a wood brace. See Figs. 12-1*a* and 12-1*b*.

DRILL SIZES

Drills above ½ inch are available in fractional sizes only. There are three sets of drills smaller than ½ inch in common use:

1. *Fractional drills,* from $\frac{1}{64}$ to ½ inch by $\frac{1}{64}$-inch intervals.

2. *Numerical drills,* or *number drills,* from No. 80 to No. 1.

3. *Letter, or alphabetical, drills,* from *A* to *Z*.

Note, in Table 12-1, that all three dovetail one another with no two drills exactly the same size. The size is stamped on the shank. If this is worn off, the size can be measured with a drill gauge, as shown in Fig. 12-2, or by checking across the margins with a micrometer.

FIG. 12-1*b*. Some of the drills you will use have straight shanks, bitstock shanks, or short-set straight shanks.

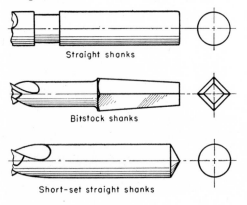

FIG. 12-2. Using a drill gauge. To check the size of a drill, insert it in various holes until you find the one into which it will just fit.

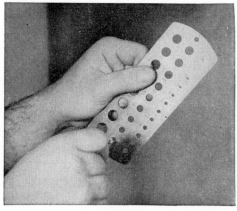

TABLE 12-1. CONTINUOUS DRILL SIZES

Diameter	Decimal equivalent	Diameter	Decimal equivalent	Diameter	Decimal equivalent	Diameter	Decimal equivalent	Diameter	Decimal equivalent
80	0.0135	$\frac{3}{64}$	0.0469	33	0.113	12	0.189	J	0.277
79	0.0145	55	0.052			11	0.191	$\frac{9}{32}$	0.2813
$\frac{1}{64}$	0.0156	54	0.055	32	0.116	10	0.1935	K	0.281
78	0.016			31	0.12	9	0.196	L	0.290
77	0.018	53	0.0595	$\frac{1}{8}$	0.125	8	0.199		
		$\frac{1}{16}$	0.0625	30	0.1285			M	0.295
76	0.02	52	0.0635	29	0.136	7	0.201	$\frac{19}{64}$	0.2969
75	0.021	51	0.067			$\frac{13}{64}$	0.203	N	0.302
74	0.0225	50	0.07	$\frac{9}{64}$	0.1406	6	0.204	$\frac{5}{16}$	0.3125
73	0.024			28	0.1405	5	0.2055	O	0.316
72	0.025	49	0.073	27	0.144	4	0.209		
		48	0.076	26	0.147			P	0.323
71	0.026	$\frac{5}{64}$	0.0781	25	0.1495	3	0.213	$\frac{21}{64}$	0.328
70	0.028	47	0.0785			$\frac{7}{32}$	0.21875	Q	0.332
69	0.0292	46	0.081	24	0.152	2	0.221	R	0.339
68	0.031			23	0.154	1	0.228	$\frac{11}{32}$	0.34375
$\frac{1}{32}$	0.0313	45	0.082	$\frac{5}{32}$	0.15625	A	0.234		
		44	0.086	22	0.157			S	0.348
67	0.032	43	0.089	21	0.159	$\frac{15}{64}$	0.2344	T	0.358
66	0.033	42	0.0935			B	0.238	$\frac{23}{64}$	0.359
65	0.035	$\frac{3}{32}$	0.0938	20	0.161	C	0.242	U	0.368
64	0.036			19	0.166	D	0.246	$\frac{3}{8}$	0.375
63	0.037	41	0.096	18	0.1695	$\frac{1}{4}$	0.250		
		40	0.098	$\frac{11}{64}$	0.1719			V	0.377
62	0.038	39	0.0995	17	0.173	E	0.250	W	0.386
61	0.039	38	0.1015			F	0.257	$\frac{25}{64}$	0.3906
60	0.04	37	0.104	16	0.177	G	0.261	X	0.397
59	0.041			15	0.18	$\frac{17}{64}$	0.2656	Y	0.404
58	0.042	36	0.1065	14	0.182	H	0.266		
		$\frac{7}{64}$	0.1094	13	0.185			$\frac{13}{32}$	0.4063
57	0.043	35	0.11	$\frac{3}{16}$	0.1875	I	0.272	Z	0.413
56	0.0465	34	0.111						

COUNTERSINKS

When using flat-head rivets, machine screws, and stove bolts to assemble a project, you will need to countersink the hole (Fig. 12-20).

DRILLING MACHINES

Figure 12-3 shows a *bench-type drill press* with the parts named. Most small drill presses are equipped with a Jacobs' key-type chuck to receive straight-shank twist drills ½ inch or smaller. A drill with a tapered shank can be used only when the drill press is equipped with a spindle that has an internal taper hole (Figs. 12-4 and 12-5). Most drill presses have a step pulley on the motor and on

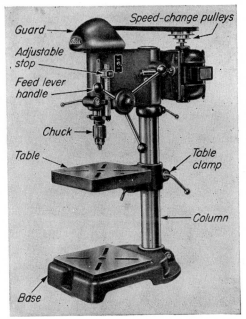

FIG. 12-3. Learn these parts of a drill press.

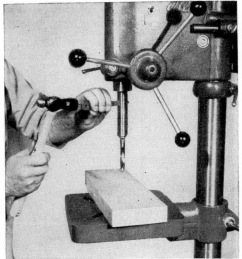

FIG. 12-5. To remove drill, force it out with a drift. Why is the wood placed on the metal table?

the spindle for adjustment to various speeds.

The *electric hand drill* (Fig. 12-6) is also excellent for rapid drilling. The

FIG. 12-4. Inserting a tapered-shank drill into a spindle.

size is indicated by the largest drill it will handle, the most common being the $\frac{1}{4}$-, $\frac{3}{8}$-, and $\frac{1}{2}$-inch sizes. The *hand drill* and the *breast drill* are not so rapid but are very satisfactory in the construction of small projects.

HOLDING DEVICES

During drilling, the stock must be held firmly to prevent drill breakage and to eliminate the possibility of injury to the operator. The best way to hold stock is to place it in a drill-press vise. (Fig. 12-7). Another way is to fasten it with

FIG. 12-6. An electric hand drill. The size is determined by the largest drill that it will hold.

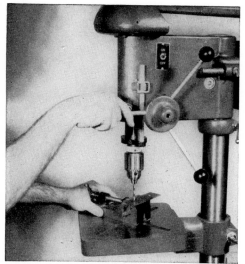

Fig. 12-7. The work is held in a drill-press vise. For flat work, this is the quickest and simplest way of clamping the stock.

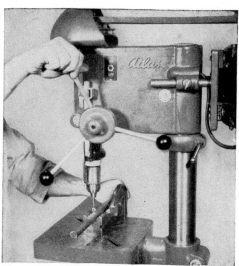

Fig. 12-9. Drilling round stock with the work held in a V block.

C clamps to the table with a scrap piece of wood underneath (Fig. 12-8). When holes are being drilled in cylindrical objects, the work should be held in a V block (Fig. 12-9). It may also be held with a monkey wrench (Fig. 12-10) or a pair of pliers (Fig. 12-11).

Speeds, Feeds, and Lubricants

Speeds for operating a drill depend upon three things: (1) the kind of drill, whether it is carbon or high-speed steel, (2) the size of the drill, and (3) the

Fig. 12-8. C clamp. When using a C clamp for holding flat stock, always place a scrap piece of wood under the work.

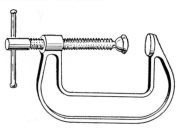

material being drilled. Generally, the *larger* the drill the *slower* the speed, the *softer* the material the *higher* the speed. High-speed steel drills can be operated at about twice the speed of carbon-steel drills.

Fig. 12-10. A monkey wrench is being used here to hold a piece of metal that has already been bent to shape.

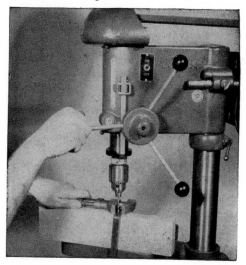

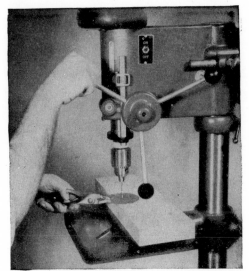

FIG. 12-11. Always hold small, thin sheet stock with pliers. If there is danger of marring the metal surface, wrap the jaws with masking tape.

Only a few changes in speed can be attained on the small drill press. Adjust the belt to one of the middle pulleys for drills of about ¼ inch. Increase the speed for smaller sizes and decrease it for larger ones.

The *feed* is the amount the drill enters the stock per revolution. Apply just enough pressure to make the drill cut into the stock but not so much that the drill burns or breaks. Likewise, do not apply too little pressure; this produces a scraping and dulling action. Apply a little cutting oil as a coolant when drilling steel.

Sharpening a Drill

In order to cut a hole in metal, the drill must be sharpened so that (1) the cutting lips are both the same length, (2) there is a back clearance from the cutting edge, and (3) the included angle

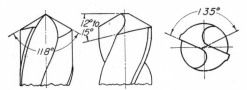

FIG. 12-12. The proper angles for grinding drills.

of the drill is 118 degrees, or 59 degrees from the center line (Fig. 12-12). To grind a drill proceed as follows:

1. Make sure that the grinding wheel is dressed. See Unit 18, "Grinding Metal or Sharpening Tools," page 66.

2. Do not turn on the grinder. Get a new large-size drill as a sample or guide. Grasp it in your right hand near the point with your left hand on the shank. Hold the lip of the drill at an angle of 59 degrees to the grinding wheel, and then twist the drill in a clockwise direction, at the same time swinging the shank in an arc of about 12 degrees (Figs. 12-13 and 12-14). Practice this motion a few times to get the feel of it.

FIG. 12-13. The proper method of holding a drill for grinding it.

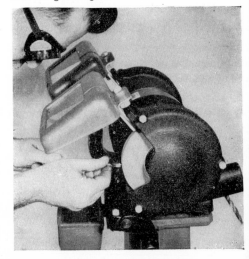

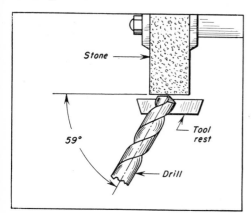

Fig. 12-14. Note the angle at which the drill is held against the stone.

3. Turn on the grinder. Repeat the above operation on both lips of the dull drill, grinding a little on either side. Check with a drill gauge, as shown in Fig. 12-15, and repeat if necessary. Keep the point cool by dipping it in cold water.

DRILLING ON THE DRILL PRESS

1. Lay out the location of the hole and center-punch it.

Fig. 12-15. Checking the point with the drill gauge. Make sure that it is ground at the proper angle and that the length of lip is the same on either side.

2. Select the proper size of drill. Your drawing will indicate this.

3. Insert the drill in the chuck and tighten with a key (Fig. 12-16). *Always remove the key immediately.*

4. Lock the work in a vise, clamp it to the bed with C clamps, or hold it with a monkey wrench or pliers.

5. Check the setup: properly tightened drill, correct speed, correct table height to permit the hole to be drilled completely through if necessary, and scrap wood or an open space between the stock and the table so you will not drill into the table.

6. Lower the drill until it just touches the metal. Be sure that the center-punch mark is directly under the point of the drill. Now release the drill slightly and apply a little cutting oil to the hole. No oil is needed on cast iron.

7. Feed the drill into the hole. When it is cutting correctly on most metals (except cast iron) thin ribbons of metal rise through the flutes from the hole.

Fig. 12-16. Tightening a drill in a chuck. What is the danger created by leaving the key in the chuck?

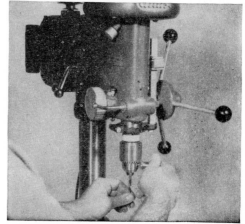

When drilling a deep hole, release the drill several times, and apply oil to aid in cleaning out the hole and to cool the drill.

8. Be especially careful as the point of the drill goes through the metal. Release the feed slightly. This is the time when the drill tends to catch and break or to spin the stock around.

9. Check the hole. Is it drilled in the proper location? Is it the correct size? Is the inside surface of the hole smooth and the underside of the metal free of a burr? Correct any mistakes the next time.

10. When drilling holes larger than $\frac{3}{8}$ inch, first drill a smaller hole, called a *pilot hole*. The pilot hole should be equal to, or slightly larger than, the web of the larger drill since the web itself provides no cutting action.

11. When drilling round stock, hold the work in a V block (Fig. 12-9).

FIG. 12-17. The correct setup when drilling a scroll. See how simple it is to swing the bed out of the way and to clamp a small, round stick to the bed to support the metal.

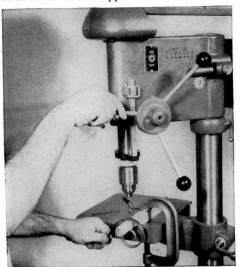

12. To drill a hole in a scroll, first clamp a small wooden rod to the bed. Swing the bed out of the way with the extended rod under the drill. Hold the scroll over the rod for support while the drilling is done (Fig. 12-17).

DRILLING WITH A HAND DRILL

1. To insert a drill, hold the shell of the chuck in your left hand, and pull back in a counterclockwise direction on the handle with your right hand until the jaws are open wide enough to receive the drill. Then turn the handle forward to tighten the drill.

2. If the stock tends to bend, place a piece of scrap wood back of it. If possible, clamp the work in a vise so that the drilling can be done in a horizontal position (Fig. 12-18).

3. Place the point of the drill in the center-punch mark, and check to see that the hand drill is square with the surface of the metal.

4. Drill the hole as described above.

DRILLING WITH ELECTRIC HAND DRILL

It is extremely difficult to get the electric drill started correctly with the power turned on, and two additional steps must, therefore, be taken. First, with the

FIG. 12-18. Make certain that you are holding the hand drill square with the work. Support the back of thin stock with a piece of wood.

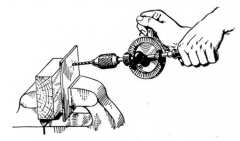

FIG. 12-19. The forward pressure is applied with the right hand while the left hand guides the drill.

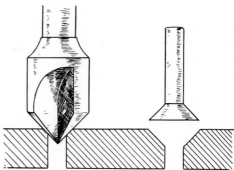

FIG. 12-20. The hole is properly countersunk when the opening at the top is the same as the largest diameter of the rivet head.

power turned off, place the point of the drill in the center-punch hole, and then turn the drill chuck by hand, applying pressure to start the drill. Second, as you drill, guide the electric hand drill carefully, applying forward pressure with the right hand, holding the drill back and steadying it with the left hand (Fig. 12-19).

It is especially easy to break a drill since the slightest jerk will catch it and break it off.

COUNTERSINKING

If flat-head rivets, machine screws, or stove bolts are used, the hole must be countersunk. Insert the countersink in the chuck and adjust for slower speed, about half that for drilling. Lower the countersink slowly, cutting into the metal a little at a time. Check the hole for correct size by inverting the rivet, machine screw, or bolt over the hole (Fig. 12-20). Rough countersinking can be done by using a large drill, although it is not a recommended practice.

Discussion Topics

1. Sketch a drill and name the parts.
2. For what kind of metal is a high-speed-steel drill best suited?
3. What kind of shank has a drill $\frac{1}{2}$ inch or less in size?
4. Describe drill sizes for those above $\frac{1}{2}$ inch. For those below $\frac{1}{2}$ inch.
5. In what ways is work held for drilling?
6. How do you know how fast to operate the drill?
7. Define "feed."
8. Tell how to sharpen a drill.
9. How would you operate the drill press when drilling a deep hole?
10. What must be done to keep the drill from breaking?
11. Can holes be drilled in rods or pipes? In a scroll? How?
12. What must be done to get the hole started when drilling with an electric hand drill?
13. What is a "countersink"?

Unit 13. Filing Metal

A file is a hardened-steel tool with chisel-like teeth used for shaping and smoothing metal surfaces. A good metalworker has a variety of files and uses each for a specific purpose.

FILES

The parts of a file are shown in Fig. 13-1. Notice that the length is measured from the point to the heel and does not include the tang. All can be classified by four factors:

1. *Length.* Files are available in lengths from 3 to 20 inches, the common lengths being 6, 10, and 12 inches.

2. *Shape.* The cross-sectional shapes are rectangular, square, round, half-round, and triangular. Frequently the name of the file indicates its shape. For example, a mill file is rectangular, while a rattail is round.

3. *Type of cut.* Single-cut files have teeth cut at an angle of about 65 to 80 degrees across either face (Fig. 13-2). This cut of file produces the smoothest surface. When a second row of teeth is

cut at an angle to the first row, forming many sharp points, it is a *double-cut* file (Fig. 13-3). This type removes metal faster but leaves a rougher surface. The *rasp cut* has individually shaped teeth and is used only on very soft metal.

4. *Coarseness.* The same kind of file is made in various degrees of coarseness ranging from very coarse, called *rough,* to very fine, called *dead smooth.* The three most common degrees of coarseness are *bastard,* which is quite coarse, *second cut,* which is medium coarse, and *smooth,* which is fine.

All four of these factors are considered when selecting the right file for the job.

COMMON KINDS AND SIZES OF FILES

Since only a few of the many different files are commonly used, you should become well acquainted with them. Remember that the name usually tells the shape and whether it is a single-cut or double-cut file (the jeweler's file is an exception).

1. The *mill file* has single-cut teeth, is rectangular in shape and uniform in thickness, and tapers in width over its entire length. The 6-, 10-, and 12-inch are the most common sizes. This file is used primarily for finish hand filing and lathe filing (Fig. 13-4).

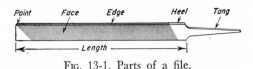

FIG. 13-1. Parts of a file.

FIG. 13-2. A single-cut file.

FIG. 13-3. A double-cut file.

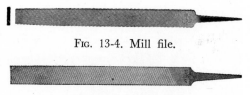

FIG. 13-4. Mill file.

FIG. 13-9. Insert a tight-fitting handle over the tang of a file. The file handle should be in proportion to the size of the file for easy handling.

2. The *flat file* is also rectangular in shape but tapers both in thickness and width. It is double-cut and is used for rough general filing. A *hand file* is very similar except that it is parallel along its edges and tapers in thickness (Fig. 13-5).

3. A *half-round file* is used for filing convex and concave surfaces. It is a double-cut file except in the smooth grade of coarseness on which the half-round surface is single-cut (Fig. 13-6).

4. A *round file,* sometimes called a rattail, for enlarging holes and filing inside round corners, is circular in shape, and tapers toward the point. It is double-cut (Fig. 13-7).

5. A *triangular file,* or three-square file, is double-cut and is used in sharp corners and in finishing out a square hole (Fig. 13-8).

6. *Jeweler's files,* in the shapes shown in Fig. 13-14, are used for work in art metal and jewelry making and for other very fine work.

CARE OF FILES

Install a good, tight-fitting handle (Fig. 13-9). The tang is sharp, and without a handle it can easily wound your hand. Insert the tang in the wooden handle, and then strike the handle on the end of the bench to fasten it securely.

Always keep the file clean. Clean your file by tapping the handle on the bench after every few strokes to remove the loose chips. Then every few minutes go over it with a file card (Fig. 13-10). Remove any metal wedged in the teeth

FIG. 13-5. Hand file.

FIG. 13-10. Stroke the file with a file card following the angle at which the teeth are cut.

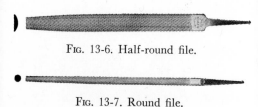

FIG. 13-6. Half-round file.

FIG. 13-7. Round file.

FIG. 13-8. Triangular file.

Fig. 13-11. Position for finish filing.

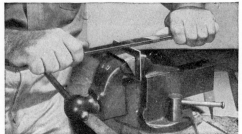

Fig. 13-13. When drawfiling, keep the file square with the edge to secure a smooth surface.

with a metal scorer, a small piece of wire sharpened to a point. Why do you need to be so particular about this? Because one small chip wedged in the file will make a deep scratch in the metal surface.

Keep your files separated. Do not allow them to lie around on the benches or to pile up in drawers. Keep them in separate holders or hang them in a rack.

CROSS-FILING

1. Clamp the work with the surface to be filed just above the vise jaws. Be sure to protect the work with soft jaws.

2. Select the right file for the work and install a handle.

3. Grasp the handle in the right hand and the point in the left hand with the thumb above and the forefinger and second finger below as shown in Figs. 13-11 and 13-12.

Fig. 13-12. Position for rough filing when large amounts of stock must be removed.

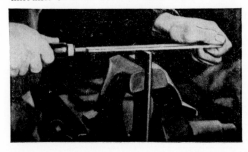

4. Apply pressure on the forward stroke and use the entire surface of the file. Apply just enough pressure to make it cut. Hold the file level and do not rock it.

5. Lift the file slightly on the return stroke. Never drag it back. Beginners often make the mistake of moving the file back and forth in short, jerky strokes.

6. Work from one side of the stock to the other to obtain a smooth surface.

7. When filing soft metals such as aluminum, brass, and copper, cover the file with chalk to keep the chips from sticking in the teeth.

Fig. 13-14. Use a jeweler's file on extremely small work, such as parts of art metal or jewelry projects.

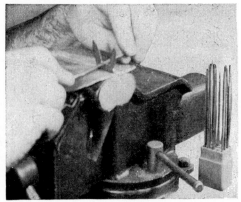

DRAWFILING

1. Select a single-cut mill file, and attach a handle.

2. Grasp the handle in your left hand and the body of the file in your right hand as shown in Fig. 13-13. Hold it at right angles to the work.

3. Using the surface near the handle, draw the file toward you. The thin chips of metal will be sheared off, leaving a very smooth surface.

4. After each cut, move the file slightly to the left to expose a new surface. Do this until you have used the entire face and then clean it. *Keep the file clean.* Remember that a single chip can scratch the surface so badly that a great deal of additional filing is required to remove the scratch.

5. To polish the surface, see Unit 17, "Using Abrasives for Hand Finishing and Buffing," page 64.

FINE FILING

Be especially careful when working with these small files as it is very easy to break them.

1. Fasten the work in the vise. If the metal is thin sheet, place it between two pieces of plywood.

2. Select the correct shape of file for the work. No handle is needed since the tang is large and round in shape.

3. To file a concave or round opening, twist the file slightly as the forward stroke is made (Fig. 13-14).

Discussion Topics

1. Sketch a file and name the parts.

2. What are the four things you must know about files in order to identify them?

3. Make an outline and cross-sectional sketch of a mill file. Of a flat file. Of a half-round file. Of a round file. Of a triangular file. After each, tell its use.

4. Why must the file be equipped with a handle?

5. How can files be kept clean and in good condition?

6. Should the entire surface of the file be used for cross-filing? Is pressure applied on the forward or backward stroke?

Unit 14. Bending and Twisting Metal

Band and strap iron of mild steel and most nonferrous metals $\frac{1}{4}$ inch or less in thickness can be bent cold. However, there is quite a trick to making a clean, 90-degree angle bend.

MAKING ANGULAR BENDS

1. Determine the length of material needed. Add an amount equal to one half the thickness of the metal for each bend to be made. If there is more than one bend, determine the order of bending (Fig. 14-1).

2. Lay out the location of the bend, remembering that the extra material allowed for the bend must be above the jaws of the vise.

3. Fasten the stock vertically in the

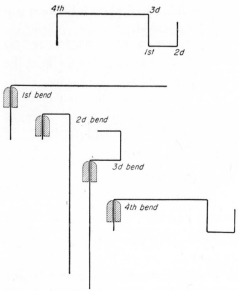

FIG. 14-1. Note the order in which the bends are made. How much extra stock is needed if the metal is ⅛-inch thick?

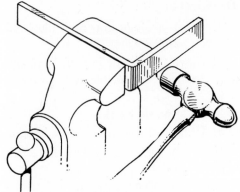

FIG. 14-3. Squaring off a bend. Note that the work is held in a vise with the edge parallel to the top of the jaws. In this way, an accurate right-angle bend is secured.

vise with the bend line at the top of the jaws. Check to make sure that the work is square with the vise.

4. Bend the stock by striking the metal with the flat of a hammer near the bend line (Fig. 14-2). Strike the metal several times all along the bend line to make the bend even. Do not strike it so hard that you thin the metal or kink it near the bend.

5. To square off the bend, place it in the vise, as shown in Fig. 14-3, and strike directly over the bend.

6. Make the other bends as needed.

7. When making less than a right-angle bend, you can use a monkey wrench (Fig. 14-4).

FIG. 14-4. Use a monkey wrench to bend less than a 90-degree angle.

FIG. 14-2. Start the bend by striking it firmly with the flat of the hammer.

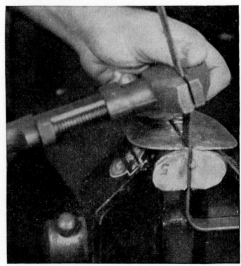

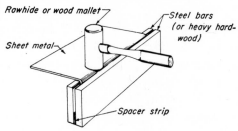

FIG. 14-5. Bend sheet stock between angle iron or wood jaws and use a wooden or rawhide mallet.

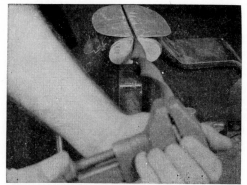

FIG. 14-6. Twisting metal. Note that you bend either a right- or left-hand twist depending upon the way in which you turn the wrench.

8. Check the bend. Are the sides straight, or is there a slight curve near the bend? Has the stock been thinned out at the bend? Did you mar the metal by forgetting to install soft jaws?

MAKING ANGULAR BENDS ON SHEET STOCK

1. Clamp the sheet stock between two pieces of hardwood or angle iron that are longer than the width of the metal.

2. Apply pressure with both hands to start the bend. Finish it with a wooden, rawhide, or rubber mallet (Fig. 14-5).

TWISTING METAL

1. Cut off a piece of metal somewhat longer than the finished piece will be. Metal shortens in length when it is twisted. You can check the amount of shrinkage on a particular size of metal by making a single twist on a piece of scrap stock.

2. Mark a line at the beginning and at the end of the twisted section.

3. If it is a short piece, place it vertically in the vise with the top of the jaws at one extreme of the twist. Place a monkey wrench at the other extreme.

4. Clamp long pieces horizontally in the vise. If you wish, you can slip a piece of pipe over the section to be twisted to keep the metal from bending out of line.

5. Hold your left hand over the jaws of the wrench to steady the metal, and then apply pressure to the handle, making a definite number of twists (Fig. 14-6).

Discussion Topics

1. What kind and thickness of metal can be bent cold?
2. What allowance in length must be made for each bend?
3. Explain how the metal should be fastened in the vise for bending.
4. How do you strike the metal to bend it. What tool is used?
5. How can you make sure the bend is square?
6. What has been done incorrectly if the metal is nicked or thinned out at the bend line?
7. How is sheet stock bent?
8. How can you determine how much extra length is needed for twisting a piece of metal?
9. How is twisting done?

Unit 15. Bending Scrolls, Curves, and Circles

The design of many projects will involve curve bending. The *scroll,* which is the most difficult, is a piece of metal in the shape of an open clock spring, or, in other words, a constantly expanding circle. It will take a great deal of care and good craftsmanship to do a pleasing job.

BENDING A SCROLL

1. Enlarge the drawing of the scroll to full size for a pattern. See Unit 9, "Making a Simple Layout," page 32.

2. Measure the length of stock needed. This can be done by forming the scroll with a piece of soft wire and then straightening it out.

3. Cut the stock to the desired length.

4. Flare the end of the stock by holding the end flat on a metal surface and striking it with glancing blows.

5. Start the scroll by placing the metal flat on an anvil or bench block with one end extending slightly beyond the edge. Use the flat of a ball-peen hammer to strike the metal with glancing blows to start the curve (Fig. 15-1). Continue to extend the metal beyond the edge a little at a time as the beginning of the scroll is formed. Check frequently by holding

FIG. 15-1. Starting a scroll. This should be done by extending the end of the metal over an anvil and striking and moving it alternately, a little at a time, until the curve begins to form.

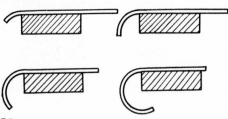

the metal over the pattern. If the curve is too tight, open it slightly by holding the curved section over the horn of an anvil and striking the edge.

6. When the first part of the scroll is complete, the remainder can be formed better on a bending fork. There are several types available such as are shown in Figs. 15-2, 15-3, and 15-4. Most of these are adjustable to accommodate different thicknesses of stock. If these are not available, one can be made by bend-

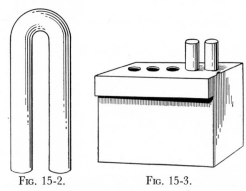

FIG. 15-2.   FIG. 15-3.

FIG. 15-2. Piece of rod bent to a U shape for bending fork.
FIG. 15-3. Metal block with pins that can be set for different thicknesses of metal.

FIG. 15-4. Bending device with the top part attached off-center to make it possible to adjust it to different thicknesses of metal.

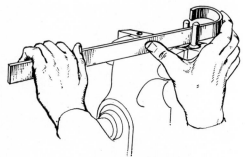

FIG. 15-5. Starting a scroll.

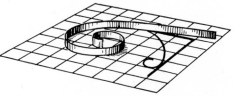

FIG. 15-7. At frequent intervals, hold the partially bent scroll over the pattern to see if it is correct.

ing a rod into a U shape with an opening equal to the thickness of the metal being bent.

7. Lock the bending fork in a vise and adjust it to the proper opening. Slip the partly bent scroll into the fork to the point at which the scroll is already bent. Now grasp the straight end of the metal in your left hand, and apply pressure with the thumb and fingers of your right hand, as shown in Fig. 15-5, to continue forming the curve.

8. Bend the scroll a little at a time as

FIG. 15-6. Continuing a scroll. Most of the pressure is applied with the left hand; the right hand is used to guide the amount of bending.

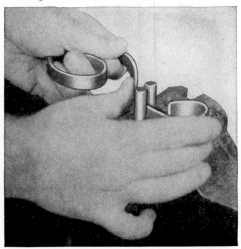

you feed the stock into the jig. Do not attempt to bend too much of the curve at a time (Fig. 15-6).

9. Constantly check the scroll as it is formed by holding it over the pattern (Fig. 15-7). It will be necessary to open the scroll a little again if it is bent too tight.

10. Often two scrolls are formed on the same piece, usually bent in opposite directions. There should be a continuous curve from one scroll to the other.

BENDING CURVES

Here are three ways to bend curves of different radii:

Method 1. Select a short pipe or rod with an outside diameter equal to the inside diameter of the curve. Place one end of the stock and the pipe or rod in a vise as shown in Fig. 15-8. Pull the stock toward you to begin the curve. Loosen the jaws, feed the metal in around the pipe or rod, and re-clamp it as before. Continue to form the curve by drawing the stock toward you.

Method 2. Lock a stake or pipe in a horizontal position in a vise. Hold one end of the stock over it, and strike the metal with glancing blows just beyond the curve of the bending device. Continue to feed and strike the metal until the desired curve is bent (Fig. 15-9).

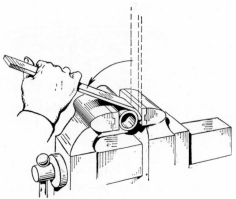

Fig. 15-8. Fasten both the pipe and the stock in the vise and draw the stock around the pipe.

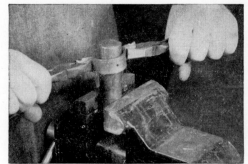

Fig. 15-10. Here is a method of bending a semicircle. Hold both ends with pliers and pull the metal around a rod.

Method 3. Fasten the rod or pipe in a vertical position. Hold the stock in a horizontal position back of it, and grasp either end with a pliers or in your hands. Pull with equal pressure to form a half circle (Fig. 15-10).

Bending an Eye

Secure a scrap piece of rod or pipe with an outside diameter equal to the inside

Fig. 15-9. Bend the rod or band by holding it over a pipe or stake. Alternately strike and move the metal, a little at a time.

diameter of the eye. Figure 15-11 shows the four steps for bending the eye.

Making Wire Rings

Secure a rod or pipe of a diameter equal to the inside diameter of the ring. Fasten the rod and one end of the wire in a vise. Bend the wire around the rod to form a coil (Fig. 15-12). With a hack saw cut the coil along the length of the rod. You will now have several rings that can be closed and, if necessary, soldered or welded together.

Fig. 15-11. The steps in bending an eye.

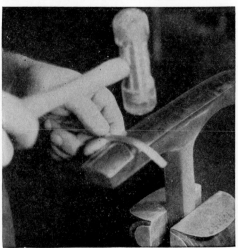

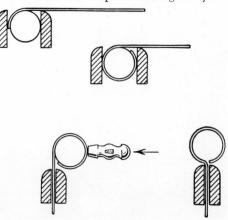

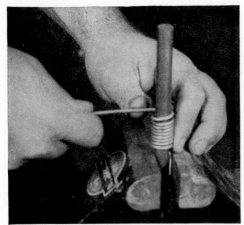

FIG. 15-12. Fasten the wire and the rod in a vise, and then draw the wire around the rod to form a coil spring or wire ring.

BENDING TUBE OR PIPE

Cut a wood form such as is shown in Fig. 15-13. Fasten a metal clip to one end of the curve. Slip the tube or pipe under the clip, and slowly draw it around the form until the desired shape is obtained (Figs. 15-14 and 15-15). Be careful not to bend the curve too sharply as this will kink the metal, giving it an unsightly appearance. If a sharply rounded corner is needed, first fill the tube or pipe with fine sand or melted lead. Bend it around a form and then empty it.

FIG. 15-13. Wood block for bending pipe.

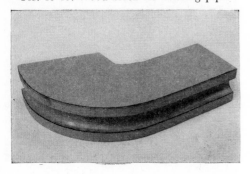

FIG. 15-14. Bending pipe horizontally.

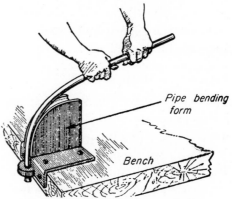

FIG. 15-15. Bending pipe vertically.

Discussion Topics

1. What is a "scroll"?
2. Suppose that the length of material required to bend a certain scroll is not given. How could you find what length is required?
3. Explain how the bending is started.
4. Why is it necessary to check the scroll often?
5. How should the stock be fed into a bending fork?
6. Describe briefly three methods of bending curves.
7. How can an eye be bent?
8. How can wire rings be made?
9. Why is it rather difficult to bend rod and pipe?
10. Is it possible to bend sharply rounded curves on pipe or rod?

Unit 16. Decorating the Surface and Ends of Metal

Most wrought-iron projects are more beautiful if the surface is peened or hammered. Beginners often merely pound the metal without any thought of the effect of the hammering with the result that the piece is beaten out of shape and the finish most unattractive. One must be painstaking in performing this process. Also, the cut end of metal is not pleasing and must be shaped and decorated in keeping with the design.

PEENING OR HAMMERING

The appearance of peening or hammering will depend upon (1) the shape of the tool used, (2) its size, and (3) the force with which you strike the metal. The ball-peen hammer is most often used, but a cross-peen or straight-peen will also give the metal a good texture (Fig. 8-11, Unit 8, "Measuring and Marking Out Stock," page 30).

1. Outline the area to be decorated. Decide whether one side or both sides are to be finished.

2. Select the proper kind of hammering or peening tool, usually about a 14-ounce ball-peen hammer.

FIG. 16-1. Peening the surface of the metal.

3. Place the metal over a flat surface, either an anvil or a flat bench plate, and proceed to strike the metal with firm, even blows which slightly overlap one another (Fig. 16-1). Do not strike so hard that the metal is stretched. If the surface is fairly wide, peen first from one side and then from the other alternately, to equalize the stretching. Every so often, flatten out the metal with a wooden or rubber mallet. The secret of success is to keep the blows firm and evenly spaced.

4. If both surfaces of the metal must be peened, either of two methods can be followed:

   a. Fasten a ball-peen hammer with the peen upward in a vise. Hold the metal over it and strike the metal with another ball-peen hammer (Fig. 16-2).

   b. Peen one surface; then turn it over. Place a piece of soft annealed copper under the metal to protect the first peened surface. Peen the second surface.

FIG. 16-2. Peening both surfaces of the metal at one time. Be careful to strike the upper surface directly over the ball of the lower ball-peen hammer.

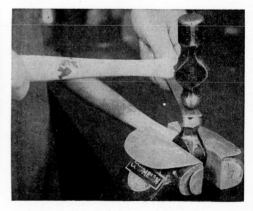

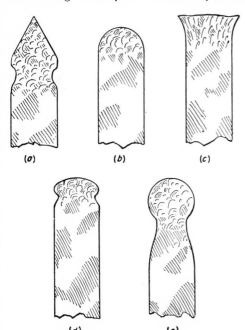

FIG. 16-3. Typical end designs for wrought-iron projects.

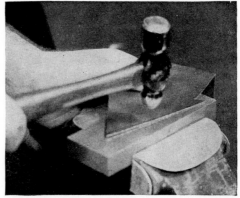

FIG. 16-4. Rippling the edge of stock by striking the very edge of the sheet metal with the peen end of the hammer.

DECORATING THE ENDS OF METAL

There are many ways to decorate the ends of band or strap iron to lend them more character and beauty. Figure 16-3 shows some of the various treatments. These usually involve grinding or cutting to shape and then peening. A typical example is the arrowhead design. To make it, first lay out the arrowhead shape on the end of the stock, and grind to the outline. Then peen the end, striking more powerful blows toward the edge of the design and less in the center. This will round off the end design.

DECORATING THE EDGE OF SHEET STOCK

The edge of heavy sheet stock can either be beveled or given a rippled effect. Hold the edge of the metal directly over the edge of an anvil or bench plate. If a beveled edge is desired, strike the metal edge glancing blows with the flat of a hammer. The rippled effect is a little more difficult to obtain since its beauty lies in uniformity or rhythm. Place the edge as described above, and strike with the peen of the hammer right on the edge of the metal two or three times in one spot. Then move the metal about $\frac{1}{8}$ to $\frac{1}{4}$ inch and repeat (Fig. 16-4). It is a good idea to practice on a scrap piece of metal before attempting a finished piece.

Discussion Topics

1. What is "peening"? What tool is used?
2. Why is metal peened?
3. Over what kind of surface should the metal be held for peening?
4. How can you keep the metal from stretching or wrinkling?
5. In what ways can the ends and edges be decorated?

Unit 17. Using Abrasives for Hand Finishing and Buffing

An abrasive is needed to obtain a very smooth finish on metal. It is important to know how to select and how to use the correct abrasive.

ABRASIVES

Many people incorrectly refer to all metalworking abrasives as emery—for example, emery cloth or emery wheels. There are two general kinds of abrasives as indicated by their source, namely, *natural* abrasives and *artificial,* or man-made, abrasives. Emery, a natural abrasive, is a dead-black substance found in many sections of the world but primarily in the eastern Mediterranean countries. Another of the natural abrasives, corundum, is very similar to emery. Both of these, however, are of rather minor importance in today's manufacturing world.

The two artificial abrasives that have almost completely replaced the natural are *silicon carbide,* made from coke and sand and bluish-black in color, and *aluminum oxide,* made from bauxite ore (the same material from which aluminum comes) which is reddish-brown in color. Both of these can be purchased in many forms, such as abrasive paper, cloth, powder, and grinding wheels. Aluminum oxide is used on steels and other high-tensile metals, but silicon carbide is better for the softer, nonferrous metals.

Abrasives are graded to various degrees of coarseness by sifting through screens of various sizes. Table 17-1 shows the grades of abrasives. Of course, only a few grades and kinds are needed; possibly the following would be sufficient:

1. $8\frac{1}{2}$- by 11-inch cloth sheets, No. 60 (Medium Coarse), No. 120 (Medium Fine), and No. 180 (Fine)

TABLE 17-1. GRADING ABRASIVES

Abrasives	Silicon carbide	Aluminum oxide	Emery
Very fine	600		
	500	500	
	400	400-10/0	
	360		
	320	320-9/0	
	280-8/0	280-8/0	
	240-7/0	240-7/0	
	220-6/0	220-6/0	
Fine	180-5/0	180-5/0	3/0
	150-4/0	150-4/0	2/0
	120-3/0	120-3/0	
			0
	100-2/0	100-2/0	
	....	....	$\frac{1}{2}$
Medium	80-0	80-0	1
	....	....	$1\frac{1}{2}$
	60-$\frac{1}{2}$	60-$\frac{1}{2}$	
	....	....	2
	50-1	50-1	

64

TABLE 17-1. GRADING ABRASIVES (*Continued*)

Abrasives	Silicon carbide	Aluminum oxide	Emery
	. . . .	. . . .	$2\frac{1}{2}$
	$40-1\frac{1}{2}$	$40-1\frac{1}{2}$	
Coarse	$36-2$	$36-2$	
	. . . .	. . . .	3
	$30-2\frac{1}{2}$	$30-2\frac{1}{2}$	
	$24-3$	$24-3$	
	$22-3\frac{1}{4}$		
Very coarse	$20-3\frac{1}{2}$	$20-3\frac{1}{2}$	
	$18-3\frac{3}{4}$		
	$16-4$	$16-4$	
	$14-4\frac{1}{4}$		
	$12-4\frac{1}{2}$	$12-4\frac{1}{2}$	

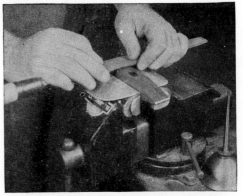

FIG. 17-1. Use abrasive cloth around a file to smooth the surface of the metal.

2. 1-inch handy rolls, No. 80 (Medium), and No. 150 (Fine)

3. Abrasive powder, No. 80 (Medium), No. 180 (Fine), and No. 320 (Very Fine)

When purchasing abrasives, you will discover that each kind has many trade names, which you may not recognize, but the abrasive can usually be identified by its color or by the description in the package.

Using Abrasives by Hand

1. Select a sheet or strip of abrasive cloth of medium coarseness. Tear a sheet into four parts. Wrap one piece around a stick or file.

2. Fasten the work to be finished in the vise. The jaws should be soft to protect the smooth surface. Apply a few drops of oil to the metal surface. Place the abrasive flat on the surface, and work it back and forth in a sanding motion (Fig. 17-1).

3. To secure a smoother finish, substitute progressively finer cloth.

4. After you have obtained a very fine finish, allow the abrasive in oil to remain on the surface. Turn the old cloth over and do the final polishing with the back side of the cloth.

Buffing Metal

A quick and efficient way to secure a smooth surface is by buffing. Buffing wheels are made of cloth or rope and are sewn tightly to make the outer edges stiff (Fig. 17-2).

1. Choose abrasive powder or grains of the desired grade of coarseness, and pour some out in a line on a piece of wrapping paper. Coat the edge of the wheel with hot glue or waterglass, and

FIG. 17-2. The buffing wheels should look like this when coated.

FIG. 17-3. Buffing metal. Make sure that you always wear goggles and that you hold the work lightly against the lower edge of the revolving wheel.

roll the wheel in the abrasive. Allow it to dry for several hours before using.

2. Fasten the wheel to the buffing head. Make sure that it is tight. The top of the wheel should rotate toward you. *Always wear safety goggles when buffing.*

3. Hold the work on the underside of the wheel, and apply even pressure as you work the article back and forth (Fig. 17-3).

Discussion Topics

1. Name the two kinds of abrasives.
2. In what forms can abrasives be purchased?
3. What kind of abrasive is used on steels? On nonferrous metals?
4. Explain how abrasives are graded.
5. How can a metal surface be hand-polished to a high degree of smoothness?
6. Tell how a buffing wheel can be coated with abrasive.
7. What safety precaution is always necessary when operating the buffing wheel?

Unit 18. Grinding Metal and Sharpening Tools

All beginners in metalworking have occasion to use a grinder. Most shops are equipped with at least two, a small one for tool grinding and a larger one for grinding metal (Fig. 18-1).

WHEELS

Most grinding wheels are made from an artificial abrasive. The abrasive grains are bonded together with waterglass, rubber, shellac, or other material, formed

FIG. 18-1. A typical grinder. This is used for general grinding and also for sharpening tools.

into wheels in molds, and then pressed or baked to make them hard.

Grinding can be one of the most dangerous things you do in metalwork, and without the proper precautions, serious injury to the eye can occur. Therefore:

1. The grinder should be equipped with eye shields.

2. There should be about ⅛-inch clearance between the wheel and the rest. If the opening is any wider, the metal could easily get caught in it, break a chunk off the wheel, ruin the metal, and endanger the operator.

3. Only the face of the wheel should be used. Most wheels are constructed in such a way that the grinding is done only on the face and never on the side of the wheel. There are exceptions to this, but be sure that your case is the exception before using the side.

4. Wear goggles or an eye shield whether or not the grinder has shields.

GRINDING METAL

1. Check the setup. See the preceding safety rules.

2. Check the wheel. Select a coarse

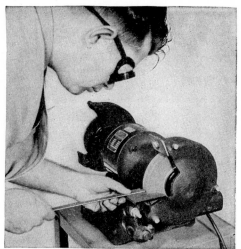

FIG. 18-2. Hold the metal firmly on the tool rest and work it back and forth across the face of the grinding wheel. Cool the metal often.

wheel for rough work and a fine one for finish grinding. If it is unevenly worn or clogged with soft metal, the wheel should be dressed before using. This is done with a diamond point or a wheel dresser made of steel disks. Hold the dresser firmly on the rest and work it back and forth to straighten and clean the face of the wheel.

3. Hold the work firmly on the rest and guide it back and forth to grind a straight edge (Fig. 18-2). When grinding a curve or a semicircle, swing the metal in the desired arc. Keep the work cool by dipping the metal often in water.

4. Whenever an edge is ground, a small burr forms on the lower side. Dress this off with a file or grinder.

SHARPENING TOOLS

There are many metal tools that require grinding to keep them sharp. Some of the most common ones are the prick

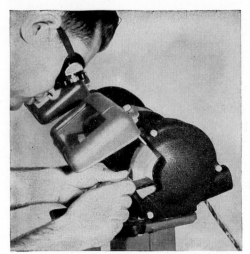

FIG. 18-3. Grinding a prick punch.

punch, center punch, cold chisel, drill and screw driver (Fig. 18-3). Always

keep one medium-fine wheel in reserve for sharpening work. The method of sharpening each tool is described in the section in which the particular tool is first described.

Discussion Topics

1. What are grinding wheels?
2. Why can grinding be dangerous? Should you wear goggles or eye shields?
3. How much clearance should there be between the wheel and the rest? Why?
4. What part of the wheel is used? How should the work be held?
5. What is meant by "dressing" the wheel?

Unit 19. Cutting Threads

One of the most interesting operations performed in metalworking is the cutting of threads. To make a lamp, an all-metal hammer, or any other project with threaded parts, you will find it necessary to use taps and dies, the tools for cutting threads. Later on in your metal-

working experience, you may cut threads on a metal lathe, but for the present only hand tools will be used.

TAPS

Internal threads are cut with a *tap*. The parts are shown in Fig. 19-1. Note that

FIG. 19-1. Parts of a tap.

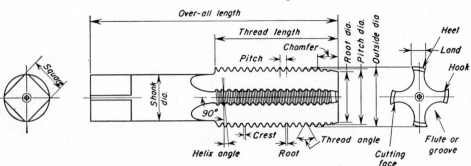

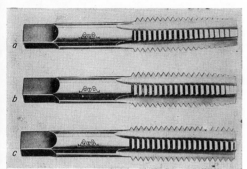

FIG. 19-2. Three types of taps: (*a*) taper, (*b*) plug, and (*c*) bottoming.

FIG. 19-4. Bar-type tap wrench.

broken in a hole, it is difficult, and most of the time impossible, to remove.

DIES

External threads on rods or pipes are cut with a die. There are many types such as the solid, the adjustable, and those made in two or more parts. The adjustable split die, shown in Fig. 19-6, is the one you will use most frequently. This can be adjusted to cut a somewhat oversize or undersize thread. The size of the internal thread cannot be changed, but you can make the external thread slightly larger or smaller to fit into the threaded hole or nut.

Dies are held in a *die stock*. Most die stocks have a guide on the back to aid in starting the threads. A set of common sizes of taps and dies needed is called a *screw plate* (Fig. 19-7).

the size is marked on the shank. Taps are made in three styles: the *taper, plug,* and *bottoming* (Fig. 19-2), and they are held in a tap wrench (Figs. 19-3 and 19-4) to do the cutting. For cutting a thread completely through an open hole, only a taper tap is needed. On a closed hole, first the taper, then the plug, and, finally, the bottoming are needed to obtain a full thread to the bottom of the hole (Fig. 19-5). *A tap is an extremely hard, brittle tool and breaks very easily.* Once it is

THREADS

A thread is a V-shaped groove cut in a helical fashion (Figs. 19-8 and 19-9). In

FIG. 19-3. The T-type tap wrench is used for small taps.

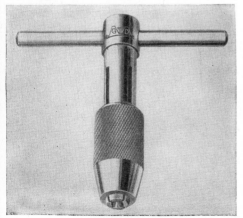

FIG. 19-5. Types of holes to be tapped. For the open hole, a taper tap can be used. For a partly open hole, both a taper and a plug tap are needed. For a closed hole, all three (taper, plug, and bottoming taps) must be used.

Open   Partly   Closed
              open

FIG. 19-6. Split-type dies. Note that the size is stamped on the die.

the early days of American machinery, many manufacturers set up their own standards of thread shape and form. This was one of the biggest hindrances to interchangeable parts. Since 1921, however, there has been one accepted

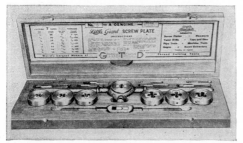

FIG. 19-7. A screw plate. This is a group of the more common sizes of taps and dies. Notice the die stock back of the dies.

FIG. 19-8. Parts of a thread.

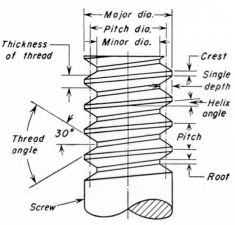

thread form for general work in the United States, called the *American National*. Note the names of the thread parts (Fig. 19-8). The two series of this thread form are the National Fine (NF) and National Coarse (NC). The National Fine and National Coarse are identical except for the number of threads per inch. For example, a $\frac{1}{2}$-inch National Coarse thread has 13 threads per inch, and a $\frac{1}{2}$-inch National Fine thread has 20 threads per inch. National Fine threads are found on most parts that require careful fitting or fine ad-

FIG. 19-9. Four common types of threads. The American National is most often used. The Acme is used on machinery, such as on the lead screw of a lathe.

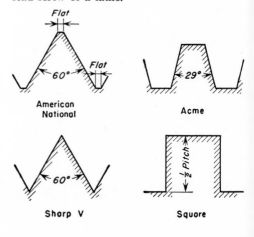

justment, and National Coarse threads are for ordinary assembly (Fig. 19-9).

Below $\frac{1}{4}$ inch, taps and dies are marked by the gauge number used for machine screws of the same size and not by the fractional number. For example, the next size under $\frac{1}{4}$-inch National Coarse is 12—24. See Table 19-1. This does not mean $\frac{12}{24}$ inch. It means that the tap or die is for a machine screw made from No. 12 gauge wire and that there are 24 threads per inch.

TABLE 19-1. MACHINE SCREW THREADS

Size (No. or dia.)	Threads per inch	
	National Coarse	National Fine
0	..	80
1	64	72
2	56	64
3	48	56
4	40	48
5	40	44
6	32	40
8	32	36
10	24	32
12	24	28
$\frac{1}{4}$	20	28
$\frac{5}{16}$	18	24
$\frac{3}{8}$	16	24
$\frac{7}{16}$	14	20
$\frac{1}{2}$	13	20
$\frac{9}{16}$	12	18
$\frac{5}{8}$	11	18
$\frac{3}{4}$	10	16
$\frac{7}{8}$	9	14
1	8	14

Now let us try to identify the kind of tap or die you would need for a drawing that specified these two numbers:

1. 8—32 NC for a hole. This means that you need a tap made for No. 8 machine screw with 32 threads per inch, which is the National Coarse series.

2. $\frac{1}{4}$—28 NF for a rod. This means you must use a $\frac{1}{4}$-inch die that will cut 28 threads per inch, which is the National Fine series.

Pipe is measured entirely differently from rods, and most pipe threads must be tapered to fit air-, gas-, or watertight. A different series called the National Taper Pipe series is required. You will find that a $\frac{1}{8}$-inch pipe tap (most electrical connections are made to fit this size) will be about the same size as a $\frac{3}{8}$-inch National Fine or National Coarse tap. This tap requires a letter "R" tap drill.

TAP DRILLS

Before internal threading can be done, a hole smaller than the tap must be drilled first. The tap drill to choose for securing the correct depth of thread is shown in Table 19-2. Suppose, for example, that you need a tap drill for an 8—32 NC tap. You will see that this is a No. 29 drill. If number drills are not available in your shop, the next best drill to choose is a $\frac{9}{64}$ drill. For the $\frac{1}{4}$—28 NF tap you would need a No. 3 or a $\frac{7}{32}$ drill.

TAPPING A HOLE

1. Select the correct size tap drill. Lay out and drill the hole.

2. Select the correct tap and fasten it in a wrench.

3. Clamp the stock firmly in a vise with the hole in a vertical position if possible.

4. Insert the tap in the hole, and then

TABLE 19-2. TAP DRILL SIZES

National Fine		National Coarse	
Size and thread	Tap drill	Size and thread	Tap drill
4—48	No. 42 (0.0935)	4—40	No. 44 (0.0860)
5—44	No. 37 (0.1040)	5—40	No. 39 (0.0995)
6—40	No. 34 (0.1110)	6—32	No. 36 (0.1065)
8—36	No. 29 (0.1360)	8—32	No. 29 (0.1360)
10—32	No. 22 (0.1570)	10—24	No. 26 (0.1470)
$\frac{1}{4}$—28	No. 3 (0.2130)	$\frac{1}{4}$—20	No. 8 (0.1990)
$\frac{5}{16}$—24	I (0.2720)	$\frac{5}{16}$—18	F (0.2570)
$\frac{3}{8}$—24	Q (0.3320)	$\frac{3}{8}$—16	$\frac{5}{16}$ (0.3125)
$\frac{7}{16}$—20	W (0.3860)	$\frac{7}{16}$—14	U (0.3680)
$\frac{1}{2}$—20	$\frac{29}{64}$ (0.4531)	$\frac{1}{2}$—13	$\frac{27}{64}$ (0.4219)
$\frac{9}{16}$—18	$\frac{33}{64}$ (0.5156)	$\frac{9}{16}$—12	$\frac{31}{64}$ (0.4843)
$\frac{5}{8}$—18	$\frac{37}{64}$ (0.5781)	$\frac{5}{8}$—11	$\frac{17}{32}$ (0.5312)
$\frac{3}{4}$—16	$\frac{11}{16}$ (0.6875)	$\frac{3}{4}$—10	$\frac{21}{32}$ (0.6562)
$\frac{7}{8}$—14	$\frac{13}{16}$ (0.8125)	$\frac{7}{8}$—9	$\frac{49}{64}$ (0.7656)
1—14	$\frac{15}{16}$ (0.9375)	1—8	$\frac{7}{8}$ (0.875)

grasp the tap wrench with one hand directly over the tap, applying pressure as you turn it. Be sure that the tap is at right angles to the work. Check as shown in Fig. 19-10. Once the tap is started,

Fig. 19-10. Checking a tap after it is started to make sure that it is square with the work.

you do not have to apply pressure because it will feed itself into the hole.

5. Apply a small amount of cutting oil (only on steel) to the hole, and then turn the tap wrench in a clockwise direction. Every turn or two, reverse the direction for a quarter turn or less (Fig. 19-11) to free chips and to allow them to drop out through the flutes. *Never force a tap.* If it sticks, back it out a little. It can easily be broken.

6. Remove the tap by backing it out. Sometimes it may stick, and if so, work it back and forth before removing.

7. Check the threaded hole. Is it a good, clean-cut, sharp thread? Are the threads cut to the proper depth? Are they in the correct position, and are the threads square with the surface of the metal? If not, check your mistakes and do better next time.

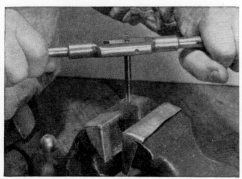

FIG. 19-11. Cutting the threads. Make sure you apply oil generously whenever you tap a hole in steel.

FIG. 19-12. Using a die. If necessary, re-adjust the die after the threads are cut the first time in order to secure a full depth of thread.

8. If you must cut a thread to the bottom of a blind hole, that is, one that is not drilled all the way through, you must be especially careful as you near the bottom of the hole. Chips will drop into it and prevent the tap from reaching the bottom. Therefore, remove the tap often to clean out the hole.

THREADING A ROD OR PIPE

1. Select the correct die. If it is an adjustable split die, it is advisable to open the die slightly with a small screw driver so that the thread cut is the largest size possible.

2. Insert the die in the stock with the tapered side of the threaded hole toward the guide.

3. File or grind the end of the rod or pipe to a beveled end so that the die can start easily.

4. Fasten the work in a vise in either vertical or horizontal position.

5. Place the die over the rod or pipe. Hold the die stock near the center with the left hand, and apply pressure as you turn the handle to get the die started.

Make sure that it is square with the work.

6. Cut the threads. Apply plenty of oil to the rod or pipe. Turn the die forward one revolution and then back one quarter turn. Proceed until the desired length of threads is cut (Fig. 19-12).

7. Remove the die by backing it off.

8. Check the threads. Are they clean-cut? Try the threaded rod or pipe in the tapped hole. If the threads are too large, tighten the die slightly and re-cut the threads.

Discussion Topics

1. Internal threads are cut with a tap. Name the three styles and tell when each is used.

2. Why is it necessary to take special care in tapping a hole?

3. What type of die will you use most frequently for cutting external threads?

4. Can you tell why standardizing the thread has made such a difference in the expansion of industry?

5. Name the common standard and its two common series.
6. How do these two series differ?
7. Parts requiring careful fitting are cut with what series thread? Parts for ordinary assembly?
8. How are taps and dies marked below $\frac{1}{4}$-inch size?
9. Explain the following: 6—32 NC; $\frac{1}{2}$—13 NC.
10. Is pipe size the same as rod size?

11. How is the tap drill chosen for drilling the hole to start the tap?
12. Is it necessary to apply pressure when starting the tap?
13. What are the characteristics of a good threaded hole?
14. Why should the end of a pipe or rod be beveled when cutting external threads?
15. What is the procedure for cutting external threads?

Unit 20. Assembling with Metal Fasteners

To assemble a project permanently, use rivets. However, in making small machine parts, you will often wish to take the project apart or to make adjustments, and in this case it is better to assemble with bolts or screws.

RIVETS AND RIVETING TOOLS

Rivets for assembling band-iron or wrought-iron projects are made of soft steel, sometimes called soft iron. They are available in flat, round, oval, or countersunk heads, in diameters from $\frac{1}{8}$ to $\frac{3}{8}$ inch and in lengths from $\frac{1}{4}$ to 3 inches (Fig. 20-1). The most common are the $\frac{1}{8}$ and $\frac{3}{16}$-inch round-head or flat-head 1-inch rivets. If the project is made of copper, brass, or aluminum,

select rivets of the same metal. The most common size for small art-metal projects is the $\frac{1}{8}$-inch round head.

A rivet set, or a riveting block, protects the round-head rivet as it is set. These come in various sizes with conical-shaped holes which tightly fit the rivet heads.

ASSEMBLING WITH RIVETS

1. Select the rivets. If the rivet is to be part of the design, a round head may be chosen, but a flat head should be selected if an inconspicuous assembly is desired. If there are to be round heads on both

Fig. 20-2. Note that a rivet should extend through both pieces about $1\frac{1}{2}$ times the diameter of the rivet when forming a round head.

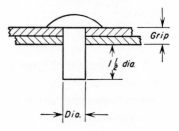

Fig. 20-1. Common shapes of rivets.

Round head   Oval head   Flat head   Countersunk

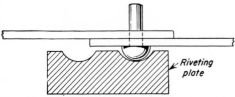

FIG. 20-3. A rivet plate or rivet set should be used to protect the head of the rivet.

sides of the project, the rivets must be long enough to go through both pieces and $1\frac{1}{2}$ times the diameter beyond (Fig. 20-2). If the back is to be flush, the rivet must extend only a small amount, just enough to fill the counter-sunk holes.

2. Lay out the location of the rivet and drill the hole.

3. Countersink if necessary. On most projects the back, at least, will be flush, but when the rivets are flat head, both sides must be countersunk.

4. Check the rivet for length. Cut off any excess with a saw or bolt clippers.

5. Insert the rivet in the hole. Be sure that the two pieces are pressed firmly together with no burr separating them. If the rivets are round-head, protect the head by holding it in a rivet set or riveting plate (Figs. 20-3 and 30-2).

6. To round off the shank, strike it first with the flat of the hammer to fill

FIG. 20-4. First use the face of the hammer to flatten the shank and then round it off with the peen end.

up the hole and then with glancing blows to round it off (Fig. 20-4). If the back is to be flat, strike the rivet with the peen of the hammer, filling in the countersunk hole, and then finish by striking it with the flat of the hammer.

7. To rivet together curved parts or scrolls which cannot be held against a flat surface, proceed as follows:

    a. Cut off a piece of scrap rod of a size that will slip into the curve under the rivet hole.

    b. Drill a conical hole about the size of the rivet head toward the center of the rod.

    c. Place the rivet head in the conical hole of the rod and do the riveting as before (Fig. 20-5). It may be necessary to open the scroll slightly to complete the riveting.

8. Check the riveting. Is the head unmarred? Did you bend your project in riveting it? Is the second head formed correctly? If the back is flush, is the surface smooth? Are the two parts firmly fastened together?

FIG. 20-5. Here is the way to rivet a scroll. A conical hole has been drilled in the small metal rod that supports the rivet.

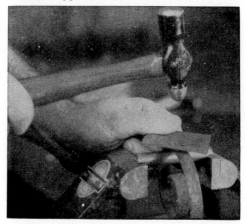

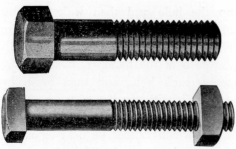

FIG. 20-6. Machine bolts.

Bolts and Screws

Two or more pieces of metal can be fastened together by drilling holes and assembling with bolts and nuts, using wrenches, screw drivers, or pliers.

1. Most machinery is assembled with *machine bolts* (Fig. 20-6). These are made in many different sizes with either National Fine or National Coarse threads and in many degrees of quality, such as rough, semifinished, or finished. An automobile, for example, has some of each type, depending upon where they are used. Machine bolts are held in place with *hexagon nuts* (Fig. 20-7).

2. Sheet-steel parts are assembled with either flat- or round-head *stove bolts*. They get their name from their original use in assembling stoves (Fig. 20-8).

FIG. 20-7. Common type of washer, hexagon nut, and wing nut.

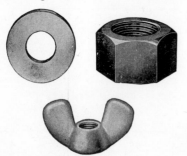

FIG. 20-8. Stove bolts.

FIG. 20-9. Carriage bolt.

Square nuts are supplied in the same box.

3. *Carriage bolts* are used primarily to fasten two pieces of wood (or a piece of wood and metal together when building such things as farm equipment and utility trailers (Fig. 20-9).

Screws are needed primarily for fastening two pieces of metal together when the second piece is tapped. The most common types are shown in Fig. 20-10. No nuts are needed for most assemblies —although nuts for screws are available. Flat- or round-head *machine screws* of steel or brass are most often used on small projects. The size is indicated by the size wire from which the screw was made (American Screw Wire gauge),

FIG. 20-10. Machine screws with round, flat, fillister, and oval heads.

Fig. 20-11. A regular screw driver.

Fig. 20-12. A Phillips-type screw driver.

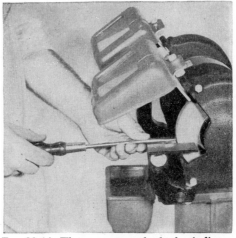

Fig. 20-14. The correct method of grinding a screw-driver blade. Grind each side so that it tapers very slightly and then grind the tip square.

the number of threads per inch, and the length. For example, a 6—32 one-inch brass machine screw is made from No. 6 brass wire, has 32 threads per inch, and is 1 inch long. Remember what was said about this in the section on taps. The most common sizes are the 6—32, 8—32, and 10—32.

Screws are set with a *screw driver* (Figs. 20-11, 20-12, and 20-13). The size is indicated by the diameter and

length of the blade. *It is very important to select the correct size of screw driver.* The proper method of grinding a screw driver is shown in Figs. 20-13 and 20-14. The common types of wrenches and pliers used are shown in Figs. 20-15 and 20-16.

ASSEMBLING WITH SCREWS

1. Select the machine screw, and a nut if necessary. The screw must be

Fig. 20-13. Right and wrong tip on a screw driver. Notice that the tip that is ground correctly tapers slightly to a blunt point.

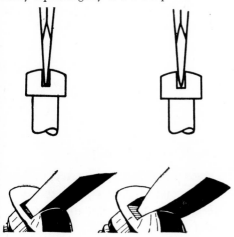

Fig. 20-15. The three common types of wrenches: (*a*) pipe wrench; (*b*) monkey wrench; (*c*) adjustable-type crescent wrench.

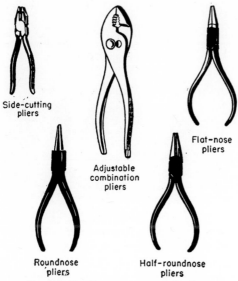

Side-cutting
pliers

Flat-nose
pliers

Adjustable
combination
pliers

Roundnose
pliers

Half-roundnose
pliers

Fig. 20-16. Common types of pliers.

3. Drill and tap the hole in the second piece. See the preceding unit, "Cutting Threads." Sometimes it is a good idea to clamp the pieces together and drill both at once with a tap drill. The first hole can then be enlarged to the clearance-hole size.

4. Choose the right size of screw driver so that you will not mar the screw head or the work. Insert the screw in the hole and set the screw.

long enough to fasten the two pieces together and, if the clearance hole is drilled completely through, long enough to extend beyond the second piece for fastening a nut. However, most of the time a clearance hole will be drilled in the first piece and the second hole tapped.

2. Lay out the location of the hole and drill the clearance hole in the first piece. This hole should be the same as the outside diameter of the screw threads. If a flat-head screw is used, countersink the hole.

Discussion Topics

1. In what shapes is a rivet made? How do you decide which size, shape, and length to choose?
2. Is it always necessary to countersink the back of the piece? Explain.
3. How are curved parts riveted together?
4. What is the difference between the holes drilled for fastening with a bolt and those drilled for fastening with a screw?
5. In installing a machine screw, what is the first hole called? The second?
6. If the screw head becomes marred during setting, what is wrong?

Unit. 21. Applying a Finish

Finishes are applied to projects to protect them from rusting and to add to their beauty. There are several ways to finish mild-steel and wrought-iron projects.

COLORING WITH CHEMICALS

To color a polished iron or steel surface, brush on one of the solutions shown in Table 21-1, and allow it to dry.

TABLE 21-1.

Color	Preparation
Black	1 ounce sulfur in 3 ounces turpentine. Heat solution in a pan of water
Blue	2 ounces antimony chloride, 1 ounce gallic acid, and 2 ounces iron chloride in 5 ounces water
Brown	1 ounce copper sulfate and 1 ounce sweet spirits in 15 ounces distilled water

COLORING WITH HEAT

Clean the metal surface, and then heat it over a bunsen burner slowly while you watch the temper colors appear. When the desired color has been reached, plunge the article in cool water. Strips or areas of color from yellow to purple can be secured in this way. Apply clear lacquer to preserve the colors.

WAX FINISH

The simplest finish for indoor projects is wax. Warm the metal slightly and apply a coat of paste wax. Allow it to dry and then rub it briskly with a clean cloth.

CLEAR LACQUER

To retain the original appearance of either bright metal or an oxide, apply several coats of clear lacquer.

BLACK ANTIQUE FINISH

For a project that has been peened, a very popular finish is antiquing. Apply a coat of black lacquer, allow it to dry, and then rub the surface with a piece of abrasive cloth. This will highlight the metal, leaving black recesses. Apply a coat of clear lacquer. With black paint use clear varnish.

WRINKLE FINISH

Many commercial metal products such as metal furniture, heaters, and novelties have a wrinkled finish which can easily be duplicated in the shop. This finish has the advantages of covering minor defects and of drying quickly. Secure the wrinkle-enamel finish in the desired color. Apply a heavy coat to the surface of the metal with a brush or spray or by dipping. Allow this to dry in the air for about 20 minutes, and then place the object in an ordinary baking oven. Heat to 180 degrees. Bake it from 30 to 45 minutes, and then turn the oven up to 300 degrees for a short time to harden the finish.

BRONZE FINISH

Many decorative articles that look like brass, aluminum, or silver are merely mild steel covered with a thin coat of powder. This powder can be purchased in liquid form or, more simply, powder can be mixed with clear lacquer and painted on the metal surface. Another effect can be obtained by applying the lacquer or varnish and then blowing on the powder while the surface is still wet. Still another method is to apply colored lacquer and then to blow on the powder to achieve a two-toned appearance.

PAINTS, ENAMELS, AND LACQUERS

A colored finish can be secured by applying paint, enamel, or lacquer. If paint or enamel is used, two coats must be applied, a primer coat and the finishing coat. For best results, apply a thin coat, brush it on well, and then allow it to dry thoroughly before applying the second coat. Some types of lacquer cover very well in one coat.

Discussion Topics

1. Give two reasons for finishing a project.

2. Metal can be colored in two ways. Name these and tell how each is done.

3. How are the colors and natural finishes preserved?

4. Does wrinkle finish require a special paint?

5. How can a finish be applied to metal to imitate aluminum, brass, silver, or other finishes?

6. Should paints, enamels, and lacquers be applied in a thick coat?

Section III. SHEET METAL

Unit 22. Introduction to Sheet Metal

Although there are only 200,000 men classified as sheet-metal workers, tinners, sheetsmiths and coppersmiths, there are several millions of metalworkers who work with sheet stock. Sheet metal ranges from a few thousandths of an inch to one inch in thickness and is made from all types of ferrous and nonferrous metals (Fig. 22-1). More than half of the sheet stock produced is used by manufacturing concerns, principally automobile, air-craft, and railroad, and in container-manufacturing plants. In these plants the metal is stamped in presses and formed to the various shapes desired. The men who work on these machines and who assemble sheet-metal parts, such as automobile bodies and air-craft structures, are not classified in the sheet-metal trades.

The worker in the sheet-metal trades uses primarily galvanized iron, tin plate, aluminum, copper and brass sheet. Their work is concerned largely with the building trades, in which they do furnace and air-conditioning installations, roof work, and metal trim (Fig. 22-2). In towns of every size there are small sheet-metal shops which specialize in installation work on new buildings and repair work on existing ones. They also build small metal articles such as containers, shelves, and aquariums for homes, stores, hospitals, and restaurants (Fig. 22-3). These men do the type of work you will learn in this area.

In addition to the fundamentals that you acquired in bench metal, you will

FIG. 22-1. This industrial-type forming roll is being used to shape a huge metal cylinder. This is the type of work done in the manufacture of large sheet-metal articles.

also learn to cut, form, shape, and assemble sheet stock in making such things as funnels, boxes, wastebaskets, cans, buckets, dustpans, and planters. Home craftsmen find sheet-metal work a fascinating hobby, in which many decorative and useful household articles can be made.

Discussion Topics

1. Is sheet metal less or more than one inch in thickness?
2. What occupations are considered part of the sheet-metal trade?
3. List five common articles made of sheet metal that you use every day.
4. What industries use over half the sheet stock produced?
5. Name three other major building trades.

Fig. 22-2. These ventilating, heating, and air-conditioning ducts are representative of the kind of work that the sheet-metal worker in the building trades must do.

Fig. 22-3. A corner of a small sheet-metal shop. Notice the patterns for common shapes of pipes and duct work hanging along the back wall. How many of the hand tools do you recognize?

Unit 23. Developing a Pattern

Before an article such as a funnel, bucket, or pipe connection can be made, it is necessary to develop a flat pattern. This differs greatly in appearance from the finished article. Many of the patterns, such as a box or cylinder, are so simple, however, that they can be laid out directly on the metal (Figs. 23-1 and 23-2).

Three types of pattern development are frequently used. *Parallel-line development* is for cylindrical and rectangular objects; an example is the joining of pipes for heating and ventilating (Fig. 23-3). *Radial-line development* is used in making cone-shaped objects such

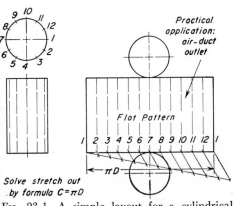

Fig. 23-1. A simple layout for a cylindrical tube that might be used for making a cup, a container, or a section of pipe.

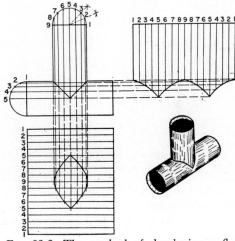

Fig. 23-3. The method of developing a flat pattern for a 90-degree intersection of pipe.

Fig. 23-2. A layout for a small rectangular utility box.

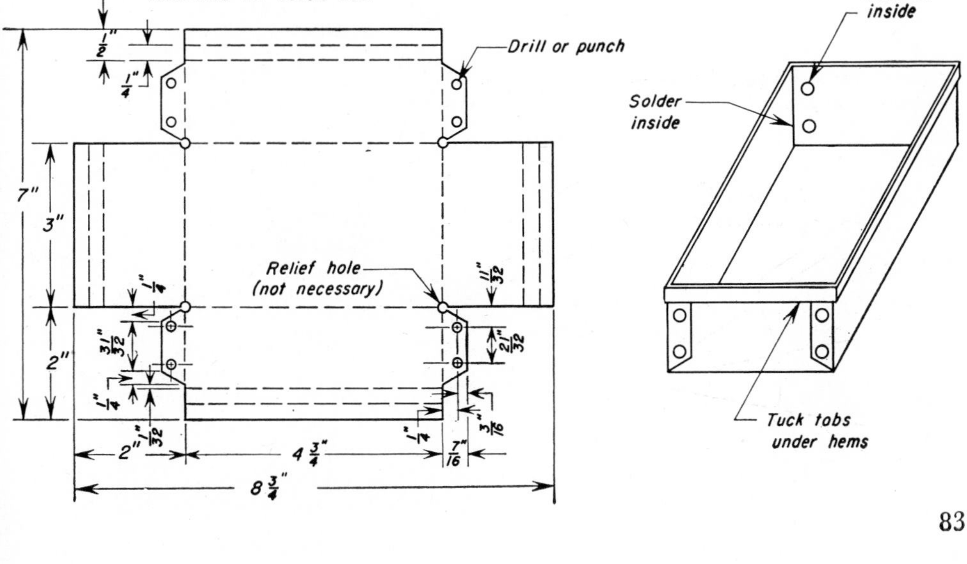

83

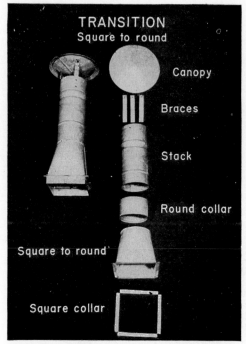

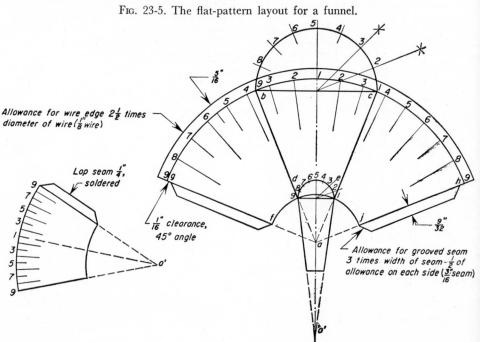

Fig. 23-4. A part which must be developed by triangulation or transition. This ventilating stack must be changed from a square to a round shape.

as funnels, buckets, and other containers that have tapered sides. *Triangulation* is used in making a transition piece, as in changing the shape of pipe from square to round (Fig. 23-4).

To develop the pattern for a funnel (radial-line development), proceed as follows (Figs. 23-5 and 23-6):

1. Obtain a piece of paper large enough to make the flat-pattern layout.

2. Draw a front view of the funnel to full size. Continue the lines that indicate the tapered sides of the body and spout until they intersect at points *a* and *a'*.

3. Draw semicircle *bc* at the large end of the body.

4. Divide this semicircle into an even number of equal segments, perhaps eight.

5. Make a flat-pattern layout for the body of the funnel as follows:

a. With the distance *ab* as a radius,

Fig. 23-5. The flat-pattern layout for a funnel.

Allowance for wire edge $2\frac{1}{2}$ times diameter of wire ($\frac{1}{8}$" wire)

Lap seam $\frac{1}{4}$", soldered

$\frac{1}{16}$" clearance, 45° angle

$\frac{5}{16}$"

$\frac{9}{32}$"

Allowance for grooved seam 3 times width of seam - $\frac{1}{2}$ of allowance on each side ($\frac{3}{16}$" seam)

draw an arc that will be the outside edge of the flat-pattern layout.

b. With the distance *ad* draw another arc using the same center.

c. Space off twice the number of segments that are on the semicircle *bc* along the outer edge. Draw a line to the center at either end of the arc to form the flat pattern *fghi.*

d. Add an allowance $2\frac{1}{2}$ times the diameter of the wire along the outer edge for making the wired edge.

e. Add an allowance on either side of the pattern for making a grooved seam.

f. This will be the flat pattern for the body of the funnel.

6. Follow the identical procedure for making a flat-pattern layout for the spout.

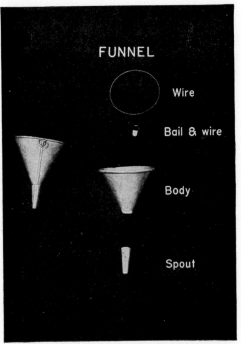

Fig. 23-6. The parts of the funnel and the assembled article.

Discussion Topics

1. What type of pattern development is used for making a funnel?

2. Develop a full size pattern for a funnel on a large piece of paper, following the steps given in the text.

Unit 24. Cutting Sheet Metal

Cutting sheet metal with hand snips is one of the first things you will do after the layout is made. Of course, sheet metal usually is in large sheets and must be cut into smaller pieces. This will be done with squaring shears if they are available.

CUTTING SHEET METAL BY HAND

Snips or hand shears. Tin snips are a good deal like scissors except that they are made heavier for cutting sheet metal that is 22-gauge or thinner. Some of the most common are shown in Figs. 24-1 and 24-2. The first ones you will use are the *straight snips* for cutting straight lines and outside curves, the *hawks-bill* for inside cutting and intricate work, and the *aviation snips*, which have many uses. These snips are made in various sizes depending upon the length of the cutting blade, usually from 2 to 4 inches in

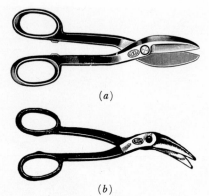

FIG. 24-1. Common types of hand snips: (a) straight snips; (b) hawks-bill snips.

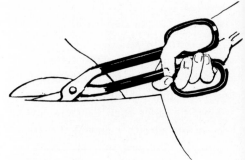

FIG. 24-3. Proper method of holding a snips for cutting along a straight line.

length. Never use a snips for cutting wire or other hard materials.

Cutting straight lines and outside curves. 1. Make sure that the layout line is clear.

2. Select the proper kind of snips and hold it in your right hand with the metal in your left hand.

3. Open the snips as far as possible and insert the metal (Fig. 24-3). Hold the straight side of the blade at right angles to the sheet. Squeeze the handle firmly, and cut until you are within about $\frac{1}{4}$ to $\frac{1}{2}$ inch of the point of the blade. Re-open the snips and repeat.

The edge should be even and clean-cut. Whenever possible, cut to the right of the work.

4. When cutting an outside curve, first rough out the metal to about $\frac{1}{4}$ to $\frac{1}{8}$ inch from the layout line. Then carefully cut up to the line and around the pattern. The scrap metal will tend to curl up out of your way as the cutting proceeds (Fig. 24-4).

5. When cutting to a corner or making small V-shaped notches, use the

FIG. 24-4. Cutting an outside curve with aviation snips. Note the way the thin edge of metal curls away.

FIG. 24-2. Electric hand shears which can be used instead of squaring shears for cutting large sheets.

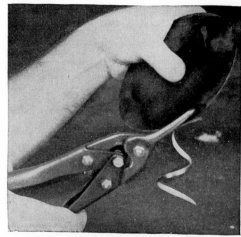

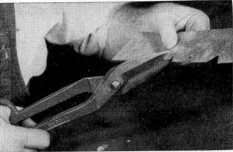

FIG. 24-5. Cutting V notches with a tin snips.

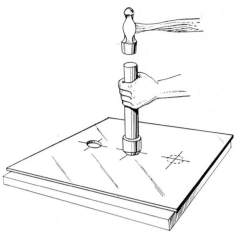

FIG. 24-7. When using a hollow punch, place the metal over the end grain of a piece of hardwood or over soft lead.

portion near the point of the blade to keep from cutting past the layout line (Fig. 24-5).

Punching large holes. Before internal openings can be cut, a hole must be punched or drilled in the waste stock. Hollow punches, which will cut holes $\frac{1}{4}$ to 3 inches in diameter in sizes varying by sixteenths, are used for this and other special purposes (Fig. 24-6). The correct method is as follows:

1. Lay out the location of the hole. Select the right size punch.

2. Place the metal over end-grain hardwood or a soft-lead block.

3. Hold the punch firmly over the layout location and strike it a solid blow (Fig. 24-7). Try to punch the hole with one or two blows of the hammer. Never tap the punch lightly because this would cut a ragged hole.

Making inside cuts. 1. Punch or drill a hole in the waste material. This hole should be large enough to admit the blade of the hawks-bill snips.

2. Insert the snips from the under side of the sheet, and rough out the inside opening to about $\frac{1}{4}$ inch from the finish line.

3. Trim out the hole to the desired size (Fig. 24-8).

FIG. 24-8. Using a hawks-bill tin snips to trim out the inside of a hole.

FIG. 24-6. A hollow punch. The size is stamped near the cutting edge.

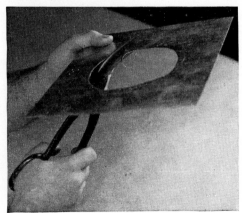

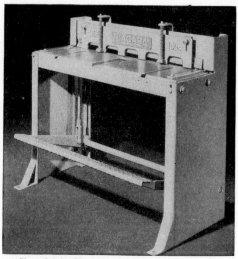

Fig. 24-9. Sheet-metal squaring shears.

Cutting Sheet Metal by Machine

Squaring shears. Some shops are equipped with foot-operated *squaring shears* (Fig. 24-9). The size is determined by the width of sheets that they will cut, the common ones being 30 or 36 inches. There is a back gauge to control the length of cut when inserting the metal from the front and a front gauge to control the length of cut when inserting the work from the back. Most squaring shears have extension arms, although these are not generally used. The side gauge is adjustable and is kept at right angles to the cutting blade. The thickness of sheet that can be cut on a squaring shears is usually 18-gauge or lighter.

Cutting metal on the squaring shears. 1. To cut long sheets, insert them from the back. If you want to cut several pieces of identical length, set the front gauge to this length. There is a graduated scale on the top of the bed for setting the front gauge to the correct length.

2. Make sure that the left edge of the sheet is firmly pressed against the left gauge and the end of the sheet against the front gauge. Hold the sheet down on the bed with both hands, and then apply pressure to the foot pedal with your right foot. *Keep your fingers away from the cutting blade at all times.* Also, never allow anyone to be near the front of the cutting blade when you are working there.

3. If you are cutting smaller pieces, feed the metal in from the front of the shears against the back gauge. This gauge can also be set easily to the desired length. *Never attempt to cut band iron, wire, or any heavy metal on the squaring shears.* This would nick the blade and afterward, every time you cut sheet with the squaring shears, the cut edge would have an irregularity in it.

Discussion Topics

1. What tools are used for cutting sheet metal by hand?
2. Straight lines and outside curves are cut with what tool? Inside cutting and intricate work?
3. Will the aviation snips perform all kinds of sheet-metal cutting?
4. Should the cuts be short or long for cutting straight or curved lines? For cutting into a corner?
5. What tool is needed for making a hole in the metal when internal cutting is to be done?
6. What machine will cut large sheets?
7. Can the machine be set for cutting several pieces of the same length?

Unit. 25. Bending Sheet Metal by Hand

There are so many ways to bend sheet metal by hand that only a few can be described here. With experience you will find new ways to do the bending. Of course, metal bending is quicker and easier on a machine, but if none is available, you can do a good job by hand.

BENDING EQUIPMENT

Figure 25-1 shows the standard *sheet-metal stakes*. These fit into what is called a *stake holder* (Fig. 25-2). Note the interesting names for these various stakes. You may be using only a few of them. If stakes are not available, there are many other things in the shop that make good substitutes, such as various sizes of rod or pipe and pieces of angle iron or bar stock.

A handy device for making bends on small pieces of metal or for folding an edge or hem is the *handy seamer* (Fig. 25-3). For the bending, always use a wooden mallet that has a smooth face since any irregularities will dent the metal. For many other operations sheet-metal hammers will be needed (Figs. 25-4, 25-5, and 25-6).

FIG. 25-2. A stake-holder plate. The various stakes may be set in these holes when in use.

FIG. 25-1. Some of the common sheet-metal stakes: (*a*) conductor; (*b*) double-seaming; (*c*) beakhorn; (*d*) candle-mold; (*e*) creasing; (*f*) needle-case; (*g*) blowhorn; (*h*) coppersmith's-square; (*i*) hatchet; (*j*) square; (*k*) hollow-mandrel.

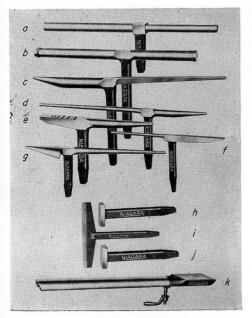

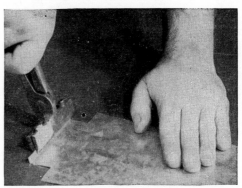

FIG. 25-3. A handy seamer. This tool is used to bend sharp angles and to form hems by hand.

FIG. 25-4. A wooden mallet for sheet metal.

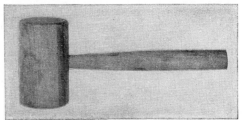

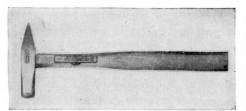

FIG. 25-5. A riveting hammer.

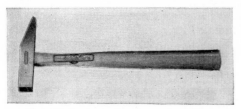

FIG. 25-6. A setting-down hammer.

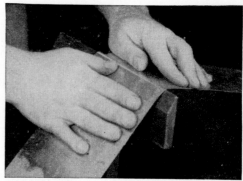

FIG. 25-8. Making a sharp angle bend over a hatchet stake.

MAKING ANGULAR BENDS

1. To make a right-angle bend by hand, clamp two pieces of wood or angle iron in a vise with the metal between them and the layout line at the upper surface of the jig. Press the metal down with your left hand, and square off the bend with a mallet or with a block of wood and a hammer (Fig. 25-7). To do a neat job, take your time and bend the metal slowly.

2. Another way to make a sharp-angle bend is with a hatchet stake. Hold the work over the stake with the bend line over the sharp edge. Now press down

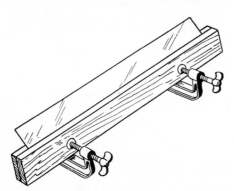

FIG. 25-7. Bending sheet metal by clamping the work between two pieces of wood.

FIG. 25-9. (*a*) Holding a wide piece of sheet metal for bending. (*b*) After the metal is bent down to a right angle, it should be reversed and the edge folded flat if a hem is desired.

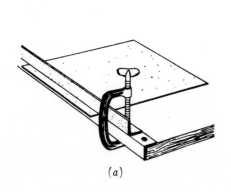

(*a*)

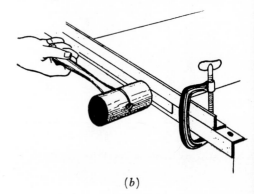

(*b*)

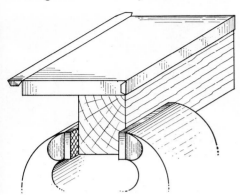

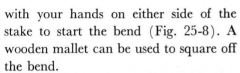

Fig. 25-10. Bending a box over a wooden block.

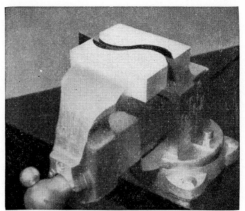

Fig. 25-11. Bending an irregular shape by squeezing between two wooden forms.

with your hands on either side of the stake to start the bend (Fig. 25-8). A wooden mallet can be used to square off the bend.

3. If a bend on a wide piece of metal must be done by hand, clamp the metal with the bend line over the edge of a bench as shown in Fig. 25-9. Press the metal down with your left hand and then strike the metal with a mallet to square off the bend. Remember, bend slowly, because if you bend one section too much a kink will develop.

4. If you are bending a box by hand, bend two ends in a vise or over a stake. Then cut a block of wood exactly the width of the box. Place this as shown in Fig. 25-10 and clamp in position. Now bend up the sides of the box.

5. To make a hem by hand (Fig. 26-2), first bend the hem at a right angle over the edge of a bench (Fig. 25-9). Reverse the stock, re-clamp it on the bench, and close the hem by striking it with a wooden mallet.

6. If a hem must be bent on a small piece of stock, use a handy seamer. Grasp the metal with the edges of the jaws at the bend line and turn the edge to the desired angle. If you are making a hem, bend it as far as it will go, open the seamer, and squeeze the metal to close the hem.

7. For irregular bends, cut two pieces of hardwood to the desired shape and squeeze the metal between the blocks (Fig. 25-11).

BENDING CYLINDERS

1. Select a stake, pipe, or rod that has a diameter equal to, or smaller than, the diameter of the curve to be bent. Place the metal over the stake with one edge extending slightly beyond the center of the bending device.

2. If the metal is thin, force the sheet around the stake with your right hand to form it. If the metal is thick, use a wooden mallet, striking it with glancing blows as you feed the sheet across the stake (Fig. 25-12).

FORMING CONICAL-SHAPED OBJECTS

When you must form conical-shaped objects, such as parts of a funnel or spout

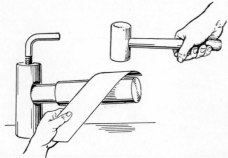

FIG. 25-12. Forming a cylindrical shape over a round rod or pipe.

FIG. 25-13. Forming a conical-shaped object, such as a funnel, over the large end of a blowhorn stake.

for a watering can, teapot, or similar object, you need a stake that has a tapered form. If you are forming a funnel top, for example, bend it over the apron of a blowhorn stake (Fig. 25-13). Force the metal around it, using your hand to do the forming or, if necessary, a wooden mallet.

Discussion Topics

1. On what kinds of devices can sheet metal be bent by hand?
2. What is the device for folding an edge or hem?
3. Explain three methods for making an angular bend by hand.
4. On what kind of stake would you bend a funnel shape?

Unit 26. Bending Metal on the Bar Folder or Brake

Metal can be bent by hand but if a bar folder or brake is available, you can do a better job in much less time. It is difficult to make a hem by hand, but on a bar folder it is extremely simple.

BAR FOLDER

The bar folder comes in various lengths between 20 and 40 inches, but the most common size is 30 inches (Fig. 26-1). There are two adjustments: (1) to regulate the depth of fold, turn in or out the gauge-adjusting screw knob, and (2) to regulate the sharpness or roundness of

the fold, loosen nuts on the back of the folder and lower the wing. Most of the time the bar folder is set to make a sharp bend since most of your work will be making a hem or fold. The back wing is lowered when the bar folder is used to make a rounded fold in preparation for a wire edge. There are stops at the left end of the bar folder which will limit the amount of fold to 45 degrees, and another stop for 90 degrees, as well as an adjustable collar which can be set for any angle. Figure 26-2 shows the common bends that can be made on a bar folder.

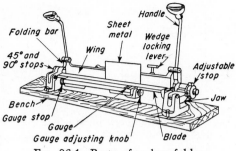

Fig. 26-1. Parts of a bar folder.

MAKING A FOLD OR HEM

A *single hem* is made to stiffen an article and to conceal a sharp edge (Fig. 26-2*b*). A *double hem* is needed when you are making a large project which requires added stiffness at the edge (Fig. 26-2*c*). A *fold* must be made in preparation for making a folded or grooved seam.

1. Adjust for the proper amount of fold by turning the adjusting thumb screw in or out until the depth is shown on the gauge. Also check the position of the back wing for the correct kind of bend. If a 45- or 90-degree bend is desired, set the stop. Make a trial fold to check the operation of the machine.

2. Insert the metal in the folder and hold it firmly in place with your left hand.

Fig. 26-2. Some common bends that can be made on a bar folder.

Fig. 26-3. Using a bar folder.

3. Pull up on the handle with your right hand until the desired amount of fold is obtained (Fig. 26-3).

4. If a hem is being made, remove the metal from the folder and place it on the flat bed with the hem upward. Then flatten the hem.

BRAKES

The *cornice brake* is used for making bends and folded edges on larger pieces of stock. The size of this machine is indicated by its length, for example, the 5-foot or 7-foot brake (Fig. 26-4). This machine is relatively simple to operate.

1. Lift the clamping bar handles and insert the metal in the brake. Tighten the

Fig. 26-4. Cornice brake.

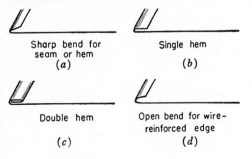

| Sharp bend for seam or hem (*a*) | Single hem (*b*) |
| Double hem (*c*) | Open bend for wire-reinforced edge (*d*) |

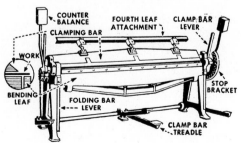

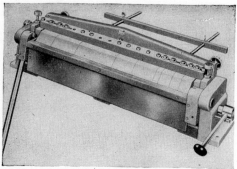

FIG. 26-5. A box-and-pan brake.

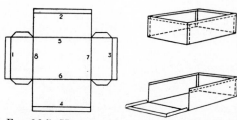

FIG. 26-7. How the hem and all four sides of the box may be formed on a box-and-pan brake. Note the order of bending.

bar handles with the layout line directly under the front edge of the upper jaw. It is a good idea to check the one edge of

FIG. 26-6. Some of the common shapes that can be made on a box-and-pan brake. The advantage of this kind of machine is that all four sides of a box may be folded by machine.

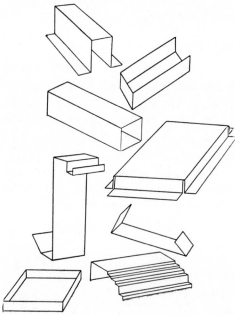

the metal and the front edge of the upper jaw with a square.

2. Now lift up the bending wing until the desired angle of bend is secured. Go a few degrees past the desired fold angle because the metal tends to spring back.

This kind of brake works well for most jobs, but it is difficult, if not impossible, to bend all four sides of a box on this machine. A *box and pan brake* (Figs. 26-5 and 26-6) is very useful. The upper jaw is made up of various widths of removable fingers. You need to use only the number of fingers necessary for the length of bend to be made. Figure 26-7 shows the steps in bending all four sides of a box.

Discussion Topics

1. Can any degree of bend be done on the bar folder?
2. What kind of hem would you bend to greatly strengthen the edge? To conceal a rough edge?
3. Can a box be bent on the cornice brake?

Unit 27. Forming Sheet Metal on the Forming Rolls

The quickest and easiest way to form cylinders and cones is with the slip-roll forming machine, more commonly called *forming rolls*. Like many other sheet-metal machines, it is not difficult to use, but there is quite a trick to doing a good job.

SLIP-ROLL FORMING MACHINE

The standard-size forming rolls has 1-inch rolls and is 30 inches wide (Fig. 27-1). As you can see, this machine has three rolls, the front two, which are gear-operated by turning the handle, and the back one, which is the idler roll. The back roll does the actual forming. The lower front roll can be moved up and down by the two front adjusting screws for accommodating different thicknesses of metal, and the back roll can be moved up and down to form larger or smaller shaped cylinders. The upper roll can be slipped out of place to remove the cylinder after it has been formed. The lower roll and the back roll have grooves cut along the right sides for forming wire or forming cylinders when the wire edge is already installed.

FORMING A CYLINDER

1. Lock the slip roll in position, and then adjust the lower roll to a position parallel to the upper roll, leaving just enough clearance between for the metal to slip in under slight pressure. Now adjust the back roll to the approximate position you think will be needed to form the size cylinder desired. Make sure that the back roll is parallel to the other rolls.

2. Insert the sheet metal in the front rolls and turn the handle forward. Just as the metal enters, raise it slightly to start the forming, and then lower it to catch the rear roll (Figs. 27-2 and 27-3). Continue to turn the handle to shape the cylinder. If the cylinder is not the right size, turn the handle in the opposite direction and readjust the back roll to correct it. When the cylinder is formed, release the upper, or slip roll, and remove the metal.

3. If there is a fold on both edges for making a folded or grooved seam on the

(a)   (b)

FIG. 27-2. Forming a cylinder: (*a*) sheet metal enters the top and bottom roll; (*b*) the sheet is raised slightly with the left hand to start the cylinder.

FIG. 27-3. The back roll begins to form the cylinder.

FIG. 27-1. Forming rolls with the parts named.

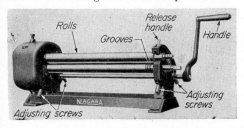

cylinder, the problem is more difficult since you cannot merely feed the work in from the front. Loosen the slip roll and insert the metal with one bend just inside the rolls. The back roll must be quite far down and away from the front rolls. Lift the sheet slightly by hand and then turn the handle. When the fold is just past the back roll, turn up the back roll to the approximate position needed to form the cylinder, and then turn the handle forward to form it. It is usually a good idea to form the cylinder slightly larger than finished size, and then to adjust the back roll, bringing the cylinder to finished size by rolling it back and forth.

4. A wire edge is often installed on a flat sheet before it is formed into a cylinder. When this has been done, adjust the front rolls with a slightly wider space at the right side than at the left. Place the sheet between the front rolls with the wired edge down and in the groove of the correct size. Then proceed as before.

5. Check your work. Is the cylinder a perfect circle or is there a flat portion in it?

Forming Conical Shapes

1. Adjust the front rolls as before, and set the rear roll at an angle that will approximate the taper of the cone with the left end of the roll nearer the front rolls.

2. Insert the sheet with the short side to the left and the long side to the right. Hold the short side as you turn the handle, allowing it to go through the rolls more slowly than the long side. This forms the cone.

Discussion Topics

1. How many rolls does this machine have?
2. Which one does the forming?
3. Will the machine take more than one thickness of metal?
4. After a cylinder is formed, how is it removed from the machine?
5. Which roll is adjusted first?
6. Tell how to insert the metal to start the forming.
7. Can the piece be inserted in the same way when it has a hem or fold or a wired edge? Explain.
8. How is a conical shape formed?

Unit 28. Making Seams

The seam which joins two pieces of sheet metal can be either very simple or extremely complicated. There have been many different kinds developed, but there are only a few that you will have an opportunity to make.

Seams

The simplest kind is the *butt seam,* which is two pieces of metal butted together and

soldered. The *lap seam* is another simple one, in which an extra amount, perhaps $\frac{1}{8}$ to $\frac{1}{4}$ inch, is lapped over and then soldered or riveted. The *folded* and *grooved seam* are very similar (Fig. 28-1). Notice that there are three thicknesses of metal above the joined sheets. This extra material must be allowed in the layout. The *double seam* is used to join the bottom to the sides of rec-

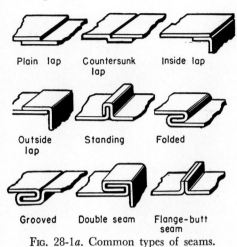

Plain lap Countersunk lap Inside lap

Outside lap Standing Folded

Grooved Double seam Flange-butt seam

FIG. 28-1*a*. Common types of seams.

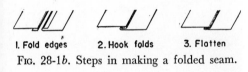

I. Fold edges 2. Hook folds 3. Flatten

FIG. 28-1*b*. Steps in making a folded seam.

I. Open locks 2. Locks hooked 3. Seam grooved

FIG. 28-1*c*. Steps in making a grooved seam.

tangular or circular containers or when making corner joints on a rectangular container.

MAKING A FOLDED OR GROOVED SEAM

The *hand groover* is a tool used in locking a grooved seam. They vary in size from No. 0 to No. 8, and each size locks a different width of seam. The No. 2, for example, is made to lock a $\frac{1}{4}$-inch seam (Fig. 28-2).

1. Determine the width of the seam and allow extra material equal to three times the seam width. For example, if it is a $\frac{1}{8}$-inch seam, allow $\frac{3}{8}$ inch. Sometimes a small additional amount is allowed for

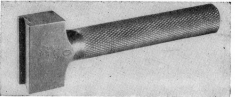

FIG. 28-2. A hand groover. The size ranges from 0 to 8, from large to small. A No. 2 would be right for a $\frac{1}{4}$-inch seam.

the rise in the seam, especially if the metal is heavier than 22 gauge. This amount should be about $1\frac{1}{2}$ times the thickness of the metal. In making most projects, add half the allowance to either end of the metal (Fig. 28-3). Sometimes it is a good idea to notch the corners to make a slightly neater seam.

2. Fold the edges by hand or in a bar folder. The metal should be bent as in making an open hem. When a bar folder is available, adjust the machine to the seam width and fold. If the seam is to be made on one continuous piece such as a cylinder, *remember to fold the ends in opposite directions* (Fig. 28-4).

3. If the project is to be some particular shape, such as a cylinder or rectangle, form it at this point.

4. Place the metal over a solid backing such as a stake if it is a circular piece or over a flat metal table if the piece is flat. Hook the folded edges together. To make

FIG. 28-3. For a grooved seam an allowance equal to three times the width of the seam must be made. For heavier sheet stock a small additional allowance is made for the height of the seam.

Fig. 28-4. In making a grooved seam on a closed cylinder or a rectangular object, the ends must be bent in opposite directions.

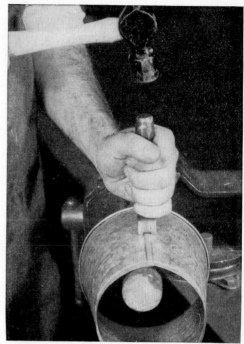

Fig. 28-5. Using a hand groover. To start, tip the groover at a slight angle and hook one edge over the edge of the seam. Both ends must be locked before proceeding further.

a folded seam, strike the seam along its length to close it, using a wooden mallet.

5. To make a grooved seam, select a hand groover that is $\frac{1}{32}$ inch wider than the seam. Hold the groover over the seam with one edge of the groover over one edge of the seam. Strike the groover solidly with a metal hammer to close one end of the seam. Repeat on the other end of the seam (Fig. 28-5). Slide the groover along as you strike it to complete the seam.

6. Check the seam after it has been locked. Are the joined sheets of metal level in height? Is the seam well formed and without nicks? Is the seam smooth?

MAKING A DOUBLE SEAM

The double seam is relatively simple when you are attaching a bottom to a rectangular container but considerably more difficult on round ones. To make a double seam for attaching a bottom to a round container, proceed as follows:

1. Form the sides of the container, allowing an extra amount for the burr or flange around the lower edge, usually about $\frac{3}{32}$ inch.

2. Turn this edge at a 90-degree angle on a burring machine, as described in the next unit, "Wiring an Edge, Turning a Burr, Beading and Crimping."

3. Now carefully measure the diameter across the turned edges. Do this at several points so that you get the average of the diameters. It is very important that this be exact.

4. Add to this diameter an amount equal to the width of the two turned edges plus a small amount for the thickness of the metal, usually $\frac{1}{64}$ inch. In other words, the diameter of the bottom must be $A + 2B + \frac{1}{64}$ inch (Fig. 28-6).

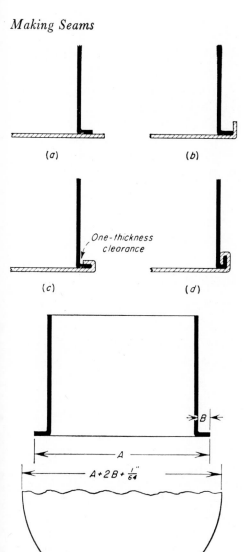

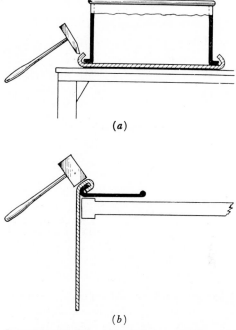

Fig. 28-7. Closing and turning a double seam on the bottom of a cylindrical container.

Fig. 28-6. Steps in making a double seam on the bottom of a cylindrical container: (*a*) the container itself with a burred edge or flange; (*b*) the bottom with a burred edge; (*c*) the double seam is closed; (*d*) the edge is turned; (*e*) how to measure the cylinder to secure the correct disk diameter for the bottom.

5. Cut a disk for the bottom to this diameter.

6. Turn the edge of the disk, equal to B, on a burring machine. You may find it necessary to practice on a scrap piece.

7. Now snap the bottom over the burred edge of the cylinder.

8. Hold the bottom of the container flat against a metal surface and close the seam with a setting-down hammer. Rotate the container so that the seam is closed gradually (Fig. 28-7*a*).

9. Slip the container over a round stake (Fig. 28-7*b*) and with a mallet finish the seam. This is done by striking the edge of the seam with glancing blows as you revolve the container until the seam is turned a quarter turn. Be sure that the inside of the container directly back of the seam is backed by the metal stake.

Discussion Topics

1. Name the simplest seams.
2. How do a grooved and a folded seam differ?
3. When is a double seam needed?
4. Draw a diagram of the different kinds of seams.
5. What tool is used to lock the grooved seam?
6. How much extra material should be allowed in the layout for making a grooved seam?
7. What size hand groover should be chosen?
8. To attach a bottom to a round container, how can you determine the size of the disk?
9. How is the edge of the disk turned?
10. What kind of hammer is needed for closing the seam?

Unit 29. Wiring an Edge, Turning a Burr, Beading, and Crimping

A *rotary machine* with several different sets of rolls will perform a variety of operations needed for making many sheet-metal articles (Fig. 29-1). In larger shops a separate machine is available for each operation, but a single *combination rotary machine* with several sets of rolls will turn, wire, or burr an edge and do beading and crimping. Some of the operations performed on this machine are relatively simple, but others are the most difficult work done in sheet metal.

WIRING AN EDGE

The wire used is made of mild steel with a galvanized or copper coating to protect it from rusting. The size is measured by the American Wire gauge, and the most common sizes are Nos. 10, 12, 14, and 18. The method to follow in wiring an edge will depend upon whether the wire is put on the edge before the article is formed or afterward. If the project is a simple cylindrical shape, the wire is put on the flat sheet before rolling. If the wiring is done while the sheet is in flat form, use the bar folder to turn the edge (Fig. 26-1). You will need only the wiring rolls. If the project is a cone shape such as a funnel, the wiring is done after it is shaped and both turning and wiring rolls are needed. Remember, in making a layout for a wire edge, to allow $2\frac{1}{2}$ times the diameter of the wire for the edge.

TURNING AN EDGE

1. Install the turning rolls.
2. Set the guide a distance equal to $2\frac{1}{2}$ times the diameter of the wire from the left side of the rolls.
3. Slip the metal between the rolls and against the guide and tighten the upper roll until it just grips the metal.
4. Now carefully hold the metal against the guide with your left hand, and turn the handle with your right hand to start turning the edge. It is essential that the metal *track* the first time. Never let it roll off the edge of the stock.
5. After it has gone around once,

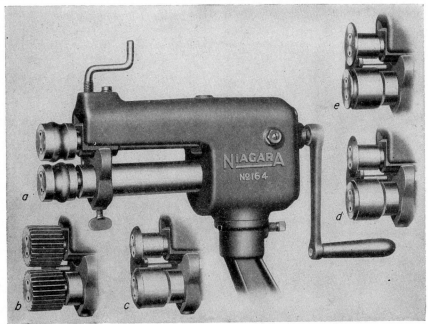

FIG. 29-1. A rotary machine with the several sets of rolls: (*a*) beading; (*b*) crimping; (*c*) wiring; (*d*) burring; (*e*) turning.

tighten the upper roll a little more, one-eighth of a turn, and at the same time raise the outside edge of the container a little higher (Fig. 29-2).

6. Continue to tighten the upper rolls after each revolution of the article, and raise the cylinder until the edge is U-shaped to receive the wire.

7. Loosen the upper roll to remove the project from the machine.

CLOSING THE WIRE EDGE

1. Cut a piece of wire to the desired length. If the object is already shaped, form the wire into a ring in the forming roll.

2. Place the wire in the turned edge with one end of the wire sticking out about $\frac{1}{2}$ inch. Then with a pliers squeeze the edge for a distance of about $\frac{1}{2}$ inch to

fasten the wire in place (Fig. 29-3). This can also be done by bending down the edge with a mallet (Fig. 29-4).

3. Place the wiring rolls on the machine. Adjust the guide so that its distance from the sharp edge of the upper roll will equal the diameter of the wire plus twice the thickness of the metal (Fig. 29-5).

FIG. 29-2. Using the turning rolls to form the edge for a wired edge on a funnel.

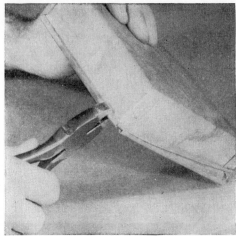

FIG. 29-3. Starting to close a wired edge with a pair of pliers. Cover the jaws with masking tape.

4. Place the project between the rolls with the wire edge up and against the guide. Tighten the rolls at the point where the edge is already turned until they grip the metal.

5. Turn the handle as you feed in the metal to set the wire edge.

6. Loosen the upper rolls and remove the stock.

FIG. 29-4. Closing a wired edge with a mallet.

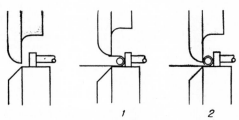

FIG. 29-5. Closing a wired edge using the wiring rolls.

TURNING A BURR OR FLANGE

The *burring rolls* are used primarily for two operations: turning a flange on a cylinder and turning a burr on a bottom in making a double seam to attach a bottom to a cylindrical container (Fig. 29-1*d*). This is a tricky and difficult operation and is not easily mastered. It must almost always be practiced several times on scrap stock.

The following is the procedure for turning a burr on a round bottom. Read the preceding unit, "Making Seams."

1. Place the burring rolls on the rotary machine and adjust the upper and lower rolls so that the distance between the sharp edge of the upper roll and the shoulder of the lower roll is equal to the thickness of metal being used.

2. Set the guide away from the shoulder of the lower roll a distance equal to the scant measurement of the burr. For example, for a $\frac{1}{8}$-inch burr adjust to slightly less than $\frac{1}{8}$ inch.

3. Bend a little piece of scrap metal into a U shape to protect your hand from being cut by the sharp burr. Place this in the round of your hand between thumb and forefinger. Grasp the disk for the bottom between the thumb (on top) and the forefinger (below) on or toward the center of the disk.

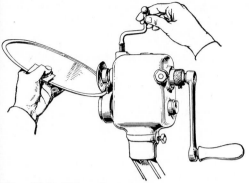

FIG. 29-6. Using the burring rolls to turn a burred edge on the bottom of a container. Note that the disk is inserted and slight pressure is applied to the metal between the two rolls.

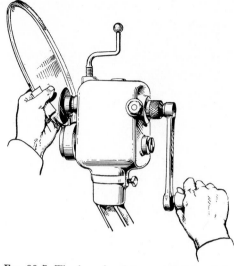

FIG. 29-7. The burr has begun to form and the disk is being raised to help form the burr.

4. Hold the edge of the disk firmly against the guide, and turn the upper roll down until slight pressure is applied to the metal. Now turn the handle slowly, carefully tracking the burr. It is essential that this be done the first time around (Fig. 29-6). The beginner usually allows the disk to escape the rolls, thus making it more difficult to track as more forming takes place.

5. Apply a little more pressure by tightening the upper roll. Then turn the handle with a little more speed as you slowly raise the disk from a horizontal to almost a vertical position. It will be necessary to continue to tighten the upper roll as the burr is formed (Fig. 29-7).

6. Loosen the upper roll to remove the disk.

7. If you have done a good job of turning the disk, the bottom will just slip over the flange on the container with a little snap.

8. Turning a flange on a cylinder is a similar operation except that the edge is turned only 90 degrees.

BEADING

Beading is done on containers to strengthen them and to decorate them with either a simple or an ogee bead. This operation is relatively simple. Place the rolls on the rotary machine and set the guide a distance from the edge for the correct location of the bead. Tighten the upper roll to apply enough pressure to form the metal lightly. Turn the handle, tracking the bead the first time. Continue to tighten the upper roll until the bead is completely formed.

CRIMPING

Crimping is done on the end of cylindrical objects, particularly heating pipes or stacks, to draw in the edge so that it will slip into the next pipe more easily.

1. Place the crimping rolls on the rotary machine and adjust the guide to the proper length of crimp.

2. Slip the cylinder between the rolls

with the edge against the guide. Apply moderate pressure with the upper roll and turn the handle to form the first impression. Then apply more pressure to deepen the crimp, making sure that the crimping rolls follow the first impression.

Discussion Topics

1. Is it possible to wire an edge, turn a burr, and do beading and crimping on the same machine?

2. What kind and size of wire is used for wiring an edge?

3. Is the wire put on the edge of the article before or after the article is formed?

4. How much allowance should be made for the edge?

5. Explain how the wire is set in the edge.

6. What is meant by "turning a burr"?

7. What is "beading"? "Crimping"?

Unit 30. Riveting Sheet Metal

Sheet-metal riveting is done to join two sheets together permanently. Sometimes the joint is also soldered to make it waterproof.

RIVETS AND RIVETING TOOLS

Sheet-metal rivets are made of mild steel and can be purchased with a black iron oxide coating or with a galvanized coating. The former are called *black iron* rivets, and the latter galvanized rivets; both are called *tinner's rivets*. The *size* is indicated by the weight per thousand. For example, the 1-pound rivet means that 1,000 of this size weigh 1 pound. All tinner's rivets are flat-head, and the length of the shank depends upon the size. These are available from small size, 8 ounce, to as large as 16 pounds. The 1- or 2-pound size is most satisfactory for 26- to 22-gauge sheet stock. This same kind of rivet is made of copper and is then called *copper tinner's rivets*.

A *solid punch* is used to punch the holes for tinner's rivets (Fig. 30-1). The punches are numbered from 6 to 10 in size and each number fits a certain size rivet. For example, a No. 8 punch is made for rivets of $1\frac{3}{4}$-pound size. See Table 30-1.

The tool used to set and head the rivets is called a *rivet set* (Fig. 30-2). These are also made in various sizes to match the size of the rivets. In selecting one, choose the rivet set by number or by placing the shank of the rivet in the hole of the rivet set. The shank should just barely fit.

The hammer regularly used is called a *riveting hammer*. It has a flat face on one side and a beveled cross peen on the other (Fig. 25-5).

TABLE 30-1

No. 6	For rivets up to 3 lb.
No. 7	For rivets up to $2\frac{1}{2}$ lb.
No. 8	For rivets up to $1\frac{3}{4}$ lb.
No. 9	For rivets up to 1 lb.
No. 10	For rivets up to 10 oz.

FIG. 30-1. Using a solid punch to form holes for riveting. Place the metal over the end grain of a block of wood or a lead block.

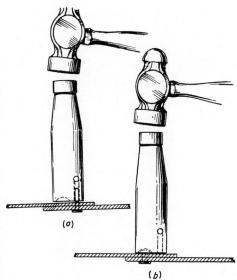

(*a*)

(*b*)

FIG. 30-3. (*a*) The hole of the rivet set is placed over the shank of the rivet and the sheets are drawn together. (*b*) The conical-shaped hole is used to form the shank or to head the rivet.

RIVETING

1. Select the correct size rivets, a rivet set, and a solid punch or drill.

2. *Lay out the location of the rivets.* If several are to be installed along a lap seam, they should be located one and one half to two times their diameter from the edge and equally spaced along the seam.

FIG. 30-2. A rivet set. A No. 7 should be used for 1-pound rivets and a No. 5 for 2-pound rivets.

3. *Drill or punch the holes.* If the metal is thin, the holes are usually punched. Place the sheets over end-grain hardwood or over a lead block, holding the solid punch over the location of the hole and striking the punch solidly with a hammer to form the hole.

4. *Set the rivet.* Place the rivet with the head down on a flat surface or on the crown of a stake if cylindrical-shaped objects are being riveted together. Slip the metal over it so that the shank comes through the hole, place the hole in the rivet set over the shank, and then strike the rivet set with a hammer once or twice (Fig. 30-3*a*). This will flatten out the sheet metal around the hole and draw the two sheets together. Do not strike the rivet set too hard and be sure to keep it

square with the work, because it is easy to dent the sheet metal.

5. *Head the rivet.* Use the flat face of the riveting hammer to strike the shank squarely with several blows. The shank will expand, filling the hole tightly, and the top of the shank will flatten a little. Now place the conical-shaped depression of the rivet set over the shank, and strike the set two or three times to round off the head (Fig. 30-3*b*).

6. If you are setting several rivets in a row, it is a good idea to punch and rivet the center hole and then to punch the other holes, riveting from the center outward.

7. Check your work. Have you dented the sheet metal around the rivet? Is the head well shaped? Do you have the rivets too close to the edge?

Discussion Topics

1. Does riveting make a permanent joint?
2. What coatings are on mild-steel tinner's rivets?
3. How is the size of tinner's rivets determined?
4. What shape is the head?
5. The holes are punched with what tool? The rivets are put in place and headed with what tool?
6. Do these tools come in different sizes?
7. How is the rivet set?

Unit 31. Soft-soldering

It is essential that you pay close attention to details when assembling projects by soft-soldering. Before you can join two similar or dissimilar metals with the alloy called *solder,* which melts at a temperature lower than the metals it joins, there are four things that must be exactly right. These four factors are:

1. The metal must be clean.
2. The correct soldering device must be used, and it must be in good condition.
3. The correct solder and the soldering agent, called *flux,* must be chosen.
4. The proper amount of heat must be applied.

If you pay close attention to these details, you will secure a soldered joint that is sound, clean, and smooth.

SOLDERING DEVICES

For most work a *soldering copper* is used (Fig. 31-1). The ordinary soldering copper is purchased in pairs, the 2-pound pair weighing a pound apiece. This would be an average size for regular sheet-metal work. They are available in smaller or larger sizes, from 3 ounces to 3 pounds per pair. The soldering copper is heated in an ordinary *soldering furnace* (Fig. 31-2) or with a *blowtorch* (Fig. 31-3).

The *electric soldering copper* is much more convenient since it will maintain

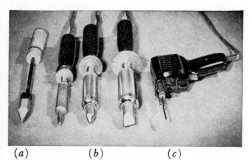

(*a*)　　　(*b*)　　　(*c*)

Fig. 31-1. Common heating devices for soldering: (*a*) a regular soldering copper; (*b*) three sizes of electric soldering coppers; (*c*) an electric soldering gun.

a uniform heat and can be used wherever there is an electric circuit. These coppers are indicated by the number of watts, ranging from 50 to 300 watts. A 150- to 200-watt soldering copper is a good size for most sheet-metal soldering, while one as small as 75 watts might be used for radio work and one as large as 300 watts for rugged work. A bunsen burner is

Fig. 31-2. Combination soldering and melting furnace.

Fig. 31-3. A blowtorch.

sometimes the heating agent for sweat-soldering (Fig. 31-4). Another electric soldering copper is the *soldering gun* (Fig. 31-1).

SOLDERS

Most soft solders are composed of tin and lead. The most common, called *half-and-*

Fig. 31-4. A bunsen burner.

half, consists of 50 per cent tin and 50 per cent lead and melts at about 420°F. Solder containing larger amounts of tin, such as 60-40, melts at lower temperatures and is more free flowing. Those with larger amounts of lead require more heat and are not suited to most soldering operations on small projects.

Solder is available in *bar, solid wire,* and the more convenient *acid-* or *resin-core wire.* The last two types have the flux in the hollow center of the wire. *Soldering paste,* containing both solder and flux in paste form, is also available.

FLUXES

In time, an oxide forms on any metal, but the process of oxidization increases rapidly when metal is heated. This must be prevented, for the oxide is a film that tends to keep the metal from reaching soldering temperature, and that prevents the solder from uniting with the metal. A *flux* is needed, therefore, to do these three things:

1. Remove the oxide from the metal.
2. Prevent the formation of new oxide.
3. Prepare the surface for a good soldering job by keeping the pores of the metal open.

There are two types of flux, the *corrosive* and *noncorrosive.* The first is more effective but must never be used on electrical connections. It must also be removed from any metal after soldering, by washing in hot water. The noncorrosive is for all electrical and electronic work, and the better commercial kinds can be used even on tin plate, on copper, on brass, and on other alloys of copper. There are many kinds of corrosive and noncorrosive fluxes.

1. Corrosive fluxes
    a. A good shop-made flux can be prepared by adding small pieces of zinc to muriatic (hydrochloric) acid until the zinc will no longer dissolve, thus making a *cut acid.* This solution must be mixed half and half with water before using and is called *zinc chloride flux.*
    b. *Sal ammoniac* in powder or bar form is satisfactory.
    c. Many types of liquid, powder, or crystal flux under various commercial names are available.

2. Noncorrosive fluxes
Powdered resin is a very good flux. Many variations of this in liquid and paste form are available as commercial products.

TINNING A SOLDERING COPPER

After a soldering copper has been used for some time, or if it has become overheated, the point is covered with oxide, which prevents the heat from flowing to the metal. To correct this condition, the point should be cleaned and covered with solder. This is called *tinning a soldering copper:*

1. File the point of the soldering copper with a mill file until the clean, exposed copper appears (Fig. 31-5).
2. Heat the soldering copper until it turns a yellow to light brown color, and then do one of the following:
    a. Apply acid or resin core solder to the point (Fig. 31-6).
    b. Rub the point on a bar of sal ammoniac and apply a few drops of solder (Fig. 31-7).
    c. Dip the point in liquid flux and rub with a bar of solder.

FIG. 31-5. The point of the soldering copper should be filed to remove corrosion and to clean the point.

3. Wipe the point with a clean cloth to remove the excess molten solder.

CLEANLINESS

Solder will never stick to a dirty, oily, or oxide-coated surface. This is one point that most beginners seem to ignore, and, if they do, no matter how well the other conditions are carried out, they never get a good soldered joint. If the metal is

FIG. 31-6. One way to tin a soldering copper is to apply a flux-core solder to the point and to rub the point on a smooth surface.

FIG. 31-7. Another method of tinning a soldering copper is to apply solder to the point and then to rub it on a bar of sal ammoniac.

dirty, clean it with a liquid cleaner. If it is black or band iron, remove the oxide with abrasive cloth, cleaning it until the surface is bright. If it is a bright metal such as copper that has stood exposed to the air for any length of time, it will

FIG. 31-8. The joint to be soldered must be perfectly clean. Here are some of the cleaning materials that can be used (left to right): wire brush, steel wool and acid above abrasive cloth, and files.

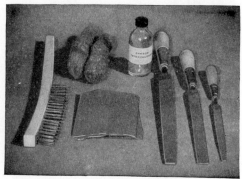

always be coated with oxide, even though you cannot see it. This must be removed before you can solder successfully. Oxide can be removed with any fine abrasive (Fig. 31-8).

Soldering a Joint

1. Place the two pieces of metal on a soldering table that has a nonconductor top such as asbestos or firebrick.

2. Make sure that the joint is held together properly. If necessary, place small weights on it.

3. Clean the area of the joint and then apply a coat of flux to it with a swab or brush. Use resin flux on most metals. A raw-acid flux is necessary on galvanized iron. If wire core solder is used, the area will be fluxed as it is soldered.

4. Heat the soldering copper to the proper temperature. You can judge this by touching solder to the point. If it melts quickly, the soldering copper is near correct heat. *Never allow it to be-*

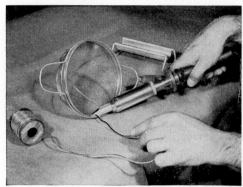

Fig. 31-10. Soldering a wire edge to a strainer using wire solder.

come red hot. Always keep the soldering copper at proper temperature.

5. Tack the joint at several places by applying the point of the soldering copper to the joint, allowing it to remain there until the flux sizzles (Fig. 31-9). Then immediately apply a small amount of solder directly in front of the point. Never apply the solder directly to the copper since this merely makes the solder run without joining the two pieces.

6. After the joint is tacked, begin at one end of the joint, holding the copper on it until the solder melts. Then move the soldering copper along slowly in one direction only (Fig. 31-10), never back and forth (Fig. 31-11). Apply additional solder in front of the point as needed. If

Fig. 31-9. Hold the joint firmly together as you tack it with solder.

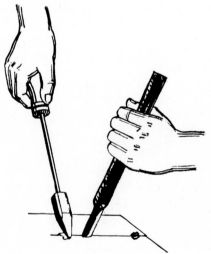

Fig. 31-11. Move the copper along slowly so that the solder flows into the joint.

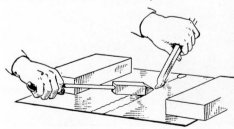

necessary, press the freshly soldered portion of the joint together with a file until the solder hardens.

7. Clean the joint with warm running water if acid flux has been used. Baking soda will neutralize the chemical action.

8. Check your work. Is it a smooth soldered joint, and are the metals really soldered together? Did you use too much solder?

Soldering a Right-angle Joint

1. If possible, block up the pieces so that the corner is in a horizontal position.

2. Apply flux at several points along the joint and tack the two pieces together.

3. Flow the solder on along the joint. (Fig. 31-12).

Soldering an Appendage

(Handle, feet, clips, etc.)

1. Apply flux at the point at which the appendage is to be attached. Then apply a little solder to this point.

2. Apply a little flux again. Hold the appendage in place, and heat the area until it is sweat-soldered in place. If necessary, hold the appendage in place with a pliers. It usually becomes too hot to handle before the solder melts (Fig. 31-13).

Fig. 31-12. Using a torch and wire solder to solder a joint.

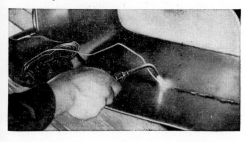

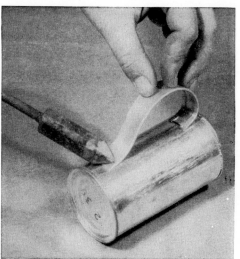

Fig. 31-13. Soldering on an appendage such as the handle on a cup.

Sweat-soldering

Many times, a multiple thickness of metal is needed to make a heavier portion of a project, for example, the handle of a letter opener.

1. Flux one surface and apply a thin coat of solder to it. Flux the opposite surface and clamp the pieces together with paper clips, small wire clips, or pliers (Fig. 31-14).

2. Hold the pieces over a bunsen burner until the solder oozes out the edge. For a neat job use a small amount of solder (Fig. 31-15).

Fig. 31-14. Make small wire clips, as shown, to hold several pieces together for sweat-soldering.

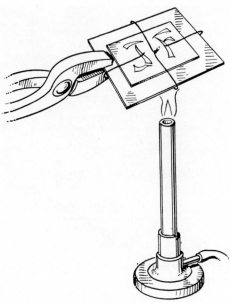

Fig. 31-15. Hold the pieces to be sweat-soldered over a bunsen burner until the solder begins to ooze out at the edges.

SOLDERING A BOX

Many projects involve the construction of a simple box in which the sides are soldered to the bottom. Sometimes both hard- (See Unit 42, "Hard-soldering a Joint," page 137.) and soft-soldering must be done on the same project. For example, the sides of the box might be hard-soldered together before the base is soft-soldered to the sides.

1. With steel wool clean the surface near the lower edge of the sides and the area of the bottom to be soldered.

2. Hold the bottom to the sides with black iron wire, making sure that the joint fits tightly.

3. Add a little flux to the joint.

4. Hold the joint over the flame of the bunsen burner until the flux boils. Move the box back and forth to heat it evenly. Re-apply a little flux.

5. Touch the joint with wire solder until it flows along the edge. Work quickly so that the oxide does not have a chance to form.

Discussion Topics

1. What is "solder"? In what shapes can it be purchased?
2. Is it possible to solder together pieces of metal that are not clean?
3. Why must the solder melt at a lower temperature than the metals being joined?
4. Name the tools needed for soldering.
5. What is "flux" and why is it needed?
6. Is there more than one type of flux?
7. What must be done when the soldering copper has become covered with oxide?
8. How can the metal be cleaned in readiness for soldering?
9. To what temperature should the soldering copper be heated?
10. Should solder be applied directly to the soldering copper?
11. Describe the soft-soldering procedure.
12. What is sweat-soldering and for what purpose is it done?
13. Why is it necessary to work quickly when soft-soldering?

Section IV. ART METAL AND JEWELRY

Unit 32. Introduction to Art Metal and Jewelry

Art metal is one of the most fascinating activities in metalwork because articles of particularly beautiful design can be made from nonferrous metals, such as copper, brass, aluminum, pewter, nickel silver, and silver. Jewelry involves about the same work except that the articles made are smaller and more intricate and are primarily for personal adornment. In a similar type of work, called *silversmithing*, tableware of sterling silver is made.

In art metal and jewelry it is possible to construct such projects as plates and trays, pins, brooches, tie clips, desk sets, belt buckles, bracelets, accessories for the home, and many other similar objects. *The design is extremely important.* In addition to the fundamental operations you have already learned in bench metal and sheet metal, you will learn about shaping and forming plus decorating the surface of metals by piercing, planishing,

fluting, flaring, coloring, and etching. In jewelry and silverware additional surface decorations such as engraving, enameling, chasing, *repoussé,* and filigree are used.

Engraving is cutting a design in a metal surface with sharp-pointed tools. Much of the engraving of initials and of letters on jewelry is done by machine; hand engraving is used primarily in hobby and craft work. *Repoussé* work is very similar to shaping metal foil in that the design is made to stand out in bold

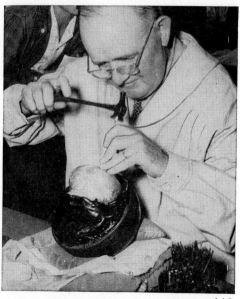

Fig. 32-1. This craftsman is doing chasing and *repoussé* on a beautiful sterling bowl. The bowl is imbedded in pitch, which supports the metal as the intricate design is worked in the surface. The silversmith is using one of the hundreds of differently shaped chasing tools (lower right) and a chasing hammer to work in the design. →

113

Fig. 32-2. Some typical art-metal projects you can make.

relief (Fig. 32-1). This is done by placing the metal over a soft substance, such as pitch, and hammering out the design from the front and back with punches of various shapes. *Filigree* is the art of bending very fine wire into intricate designs. *Enameling* is similar to making enamelware or enamel tile; pigments of various

Fig. 32-3. Copper and aluminum projects.

colors are applied to the metal surface (usually copper or silver) the article placed in a furnace, and the enamel baked on the surface. Everything from small jewelry to large bowls, plates, and plaques can be decorated in this way.

The opportunities for employment in jewelry making and silversmithing are very limited as compared with those in the other metalworking areas. There are about 30,000 people doing this work, many of whom design and make all kinds of jewelry from the inexpensive costume jewelry to the exquisite pieces of great value, which are made of gold, silver, and platinum. Silversmiths specialize in the design and construction of silverware and tableware made of sterling silver. Many, many more times the number of people employed at this work enjoy art metal and jewelry as a hobby. It is a particularly good leisure-time activity since it requires only a few hand tools and can be done in a limited amount of space. It is also inexpensive to begin, and the materials are relatively low in cost as compared with the worth of the finished articles (Figs. 32-2, 32-3, and 32-4).

Discussion Topics

1. Are ferrous or nonferrous metals used for jewelry and art metal?
2. What is "silversmithing"?
3. What is "engraving"? *"Repoussé"?* "Filigree"? "Enameling"?
4. Why does this area make such an excellent hobby activity?

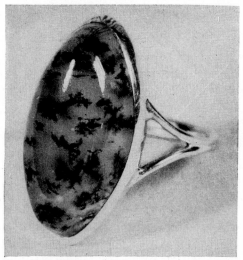

Fig. 32-4. This beautiful ring was made in one of the author's jewelry classes. The stone was cut, the set made, and the stone set. It is an example of what an advanced craftsman can make. The materials are very inexpensive but the ring is worth a great deal.

Unit 33. Tapping, Chasing, and Design Stamping

Metal tapping is so simple that you will find it difficult to believe that such attractive articles can be made by this method. Anyone can make a beautiful plaque, design on a book end, letter tray, or tie rack, for example with a little patience and a good design. The metals should be about 30-gauge tin plate, sheet copper, brass, or aluminum. If a plaque is to be tapped, you will need a piece of $\frac{1}{4}$-inch plywood and enough small $\frac{1}{8}$- to $\frac{1}{4}$-inch escutcheon pins for mounting. The tapping tool can be a simple ice pick, a center punch, or large-size nails ground to variously shaped heads. The best tools, however, are made from drill rod. After the points are shaped to differ-

ent designs, they should be hardened and tempered (Fig. 33-1). See Unit 48, "Heat-treating Steels," page 155.

Fig. 33-1. All the materials needed to make a completed tapped placque, including the copper sheet, the plywood back, the escutcheon pins, and the design.

METAL TAPPING

1. Select a design and cut a piece of metal to size.

2. Fasten the piece of metal to the plywood with ¼-inch escutcheon pins. These are round-head brass nails so small that you must hold them with a tweezers or jeweler's pliers to install them.

3. Place the paper design over the metal and hold it secure with masking tape.

4. Outline the design by tapping it with a sharp-pointed tapping tool. *Do not strike it so hard that you make a hole in the metal.* Remove the paper design when the outlines and border are complete.

5. Stipple in the background with the same tool or with a more blunt one. Work outward from the design and inward from the edge. This will keep the metal from stretching too much in one direction (Fig. 33-2).

6. Clean the surface lightly with steel wool or fine abrasive cloth and apply a coat of clear lacquer.

FIG. 33-2. The outline has been completed and the background is being stippled.

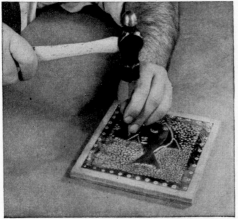

CHASING

Chasing is similar to metal tapping except that the punches are commercially designed. The design is outlined with *tracing tools* (Fig. 33-3), and *matting tools* are used to fill in the background.

FIG. 33-3. Chasing tools for various designs.

PLAIN TOOLS

TOOLS FOR BACKGROUND DECORATING

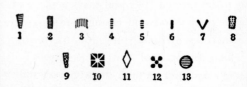

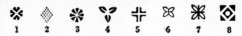

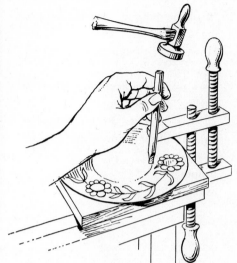

FIG. 33-4. Outlining a chased design.

A special hammer called a *chasing hammer* is the tapping instrument. In advanced chasing the work is held in a

FIG. 33-5. Working down the background in a chased design.

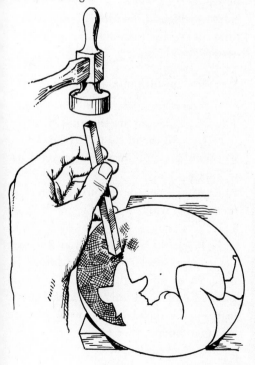

pitch block, but for simple chasing the metal can be clamped over a piece of soft wood (Figs. 33-4 and 33-5). The design is first carefully outlined with tracing tools, and then the background is worked in with the matting tools.

DESIGN STAMPING

Punches for design stamping have intricately shaped points, many of which are Indian designs (Fig. 33-6). To apply the design, hold the punch in position over the flat metal and strike it firmly with a hammer. Never force the design too

FIG. 33-6. Design-stamping tools may be obtained with these Indian designs which are excellent for bracelets, pins, buckles, and wideband rings.

1) THUNDERBIRD, SACRED *Bearer of Happiness*

2) SUN SYMBOL *Happiness*

3) HORSE *Journey*

4) SUN RAYS *Constancy*

5) CACTUS FLOWER *Courtship*

6) RAIN CLOUDS *Good Prospects*

7) SPIDER *Good Luck*

8) SWASTIKA *Good Luck*

9) MORNING STAR *Guidance*

10) ARROW *Protection*

11) ARROWHEAD *Alertness*

12) MEDICINE MAN'S EYE *Wise, Watchful*

13) BROKEN ARROW *Peace*

14) RATTLESNAKE JAW *Strength*

15) BIG MOUNTAIN *Abundance*

16) CROSSED ARROWS *Peace*

17) HOGAN *Permanent Home*

18) THUNDERBIRD TRACK *Bright Prospects*

deeply in the metal or repeat the stamping after it has been done the first time. Border patterns are very effective, and either the same punch or two or more of different, harmonizing patterns can be used.

Discussion Topics

1. What is "metal tapping"?

2. Must the metal be attached to a backing?
3. How is the design transferred to the metal?
4. How can you keep the metal from curling or stretching?
5. In what way do the punches used in chasing differ from tapping tools?
6. Is chasing done in the same way as tapping?
7. What is "design stamping"?

Unit 34. Shaping Metal Foil

Creating a design in thin metal is a simple and effective way of obtaining bold relief patterns (Fig. 34-1). The metal used is extremely thin, No. 32 to No. 36 gauge brass, copper, or aluminum. It can be cut with an ordinary shears and formed with any blunt-pointed instrument, such as a wooden dowel, leather-forming tool, or even the point of a pencil. Design of this type makes beautiful wall plaques, lamp

Fig. 34-1. These art-metal designs can be made with very little effort. When placed in the right setting, they are a most effective decoration.

bases, overlay for book ends, and tops of metal or wood boxes. Simple pictures, silhouettes, profiles, and etchings are the best designs to select.

You will need several thicknesses of newspaper or cloth or a pad of soft rubber which should be about $\frac{1}{4}$ inch thick and of a size equal to the area of the design.

MOLDING OR SHAPING METAL FOIL

1. Trace the design on thin paper. The simple designs are the most effective.
2. Cut out the metal foil to the desired size with snips or shears. Be careful not to kink it.
3. Attach the design to the piece of metal foil with tape (Fig. 9-3, page 35).
4. Place the pattern and metal over the rubber sheet or other padding. Go over each line lightly with a blunt-pointed tool to outline. Be careful not to lean on the metal as you work because this metal dents very easily.
5. Remove the pattern and turn the

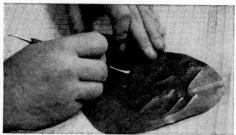

FIG. 34-2. The outline has been traced, and the design is being worked out from the back.

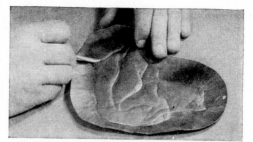

FIG. 34-3. The background is being smoothed and finished.

metal face down on the pad. With a blunt tool work the design from the outline toward the center to force it out from the back (Fig. 34-2). Do not press too hard but work evenly over the entire design. Then remove the design from the pad and place it face up on a hard surface.

6. With a flat molding tool, work out from the design toward the edge of the metal, smoothing out the background with long, sweeping strokes (Fig. 34-3). After the forming has been completed, you can further decorate parts of the design by painting them with colored enamel or by coloring the metal with a liver of sulfur solution. Last of all apply a coat of clear lacquer. See Unit

43, "Polishing, Coloring, and Preserving."

7. The back should be filled with plaster of paris support, especially if there is danger that it will be dented in use. The metal design should always be mounted.

Discussion Topics

1. What thickness of metal can be shaped in this way?
2. Name the tools needed.
3. How is this metal cut?
4. What kind of padding is needed?
5. Should one section of the design be completed at a time?
6. How is the background raised?
7. In what ways can the design be further decorated?

Unit 35. Sawing or Piercing

One way to enrich the surface of small objects is to saw out a pattern with a jeweler's saw. This is rather meticulous work when done by hand, but it is something you must learn to do well since it is so common. The same work can be done on a power jig saw much more quickly.

SAW FRAMES AND BLADES

The jeweler's frame is similar to a hacksaw frame except that it is lighter and can be readily adjusted to any length to provide for different lengths of blades. These frames are U-shaped and of various depth, some for small jewelry work and others for large patterns. Jeweler's

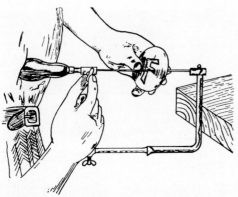

FIG. 35-1. Installing a jeweler's-saw blade. Apply pressure to the frame before tightening the second end of the blade so that it will be taut.

FIG. 35-2. Using a jeweler's saw. Always make sure the work is held firmly on a V cutting block.

blades can be purchased in sizes from No. 8/0, which is smaller than a thread, to No. 14, which is over $\frac{1}{16}$ inch in width. For average light work use a No. 2/0 or No. 1/0 and for slightly heavier material a No. 1 or No. 2 blade. These blades can also be installed in a jig saw for power metal cutting. If you do not have jeweler's frames, blades for cutting metal with pinned or bent ends are available that will fit your coping-saw frame.

CUTTING WITH A JEWELER'S SAW

1. Adjust the frame to about $\frac{1}{2}$ inch longer than the blade. Fasten the blade in one end with the teeth pointing toward the handle. Hold the frame against the edge of the bench, applying pressure to the handle with your body, and fasten the handle end (Fig. 35-1). If internal cutting is to be done, a hole must be drilled in the waste stock and the work slipped over the blade before the second end is fastened.

2. Fasten a bench pin or V-cutting board in a vise or on the end of a table so that it will be at about elbow height when you are seated. Most cutting is

done in a sitting position because you must be relaxed to do a good job.

3. Hold the metal over the V block with your left hand (Fig. 35-2). The cutting should be done in the V part of the block. Hold the saw in your right hand in a vertical position. Start in the waste stock with an up-and-down movement, using the entire length of the blade. The cutting is done on the down stroke. Try to maintain a uniform, easy cutting action, and avoid bending the blade since these blades break very easily. Come up to the layout line at a slight angle and then cut along just outside the line. Move the saw or the work a little at a time as needed to follow the layout line. If a sharp corner is reached, continue to operate the saw without applying any forward pressure and then turn either the metal or the frame. If the blade tends to stick, apply a little soap or wax to it as a lubricant. If you need to back out of the saw kerf, continue to move the blade up and down as it is removed.

4. Check your work. Have you broken many blades because you forced the blade or tilted the frame? Is the line smooth, requiring a minimum of filing? Have you cut the piece too small?

Discussion Topics

1. Describe the jeweler's frame and blades. Can blades of different lengths be installed?

2. How do the blades range in size?

3. When the blade is fastened in the frame, which way should the teeth point?

4. Explain how internal cutting can be done.

5. Should you make use of the entire blade length?

6. How can you keep the blade from sticking?

Unit 36. Annealing and Pickling Metal

While metal is being shaped into a dish or tray, it becomes hard and must be softened by the process of *annealing*. It also becomes covered with dirt and oxide and must be cleaned by being dipped in an acid bath. This is called *pickling*. During the forming operations these two procedures are done simultaneously. After the final shape is obtained, only pickling is needed. The hardening, tempering, and annealing of steel is discussed in Unit 48, "Heat-treating Steels," page 155.

PICKLING SOLUTIONS

The pickling solution is made by mixing acid in water. *Always pour the acid into the water, never the reverse.* When you are working with pickling solutions, remember that they can be dangerous and that proper precautions must be taken to keep from burning holes in your clothing, from burning your skin or from injuring your eyes. Mix the solution as follows:

1. Secure a glass or earthenware jar large enough to hold the largest project you will be making. The jar must have a cover and must be kept in a well-ventilated place since acid fumes rust steel tools rapidly.

2. Pour a gallon or multiple of a gallon of water into the jar to fill it half to three-fourths full.

3. Slowly add 10 ounces of sulfuric acid for each gallon of water, stirring the solution with a glass or wooden rod to keep it from overheating.

ANNEALING AND PICKLING COPPER AND ITS ALLOYS

1. Heat the metal to a dull-red heat. This can be done by holding the article over a bunsen burner, by applying a torch to it, or by placing it in a soldering furnace.

2. Apply the heat evenly to bring the entire piece up to temperature slowly.

3. Pick up the heated article with copper tweezers or tongs and slide it into the pickling solution. *Never drop it,* making the solution splash. The rapid cooling will anneal the metal and clean off the dirt and oxide.

4. Remove the article from the solu-

tion with the tweezers and clean it off under warm running water.

Annealing can be done by submerging the hot metal in water. However, this will not remove the oxide that has formed.

PICKLING

When the forming has been completed and you do not wish to soften the project again, place it in the solution without heating, and allow it to remain there from 5 to 10 minutes. Take it out with tweezers, wash it off under warm running water, and dry it off in clean sawdust or with paper towels. *Never touch the article with your fingers after it has been cleaned for the last time in preparation for adding a finish.*

ANNEALING ALUMINUM

It is difficult to anneal aluminum because it is almost impossible to tell when the metal is hot enough. It is very easy

to melt it or to burn a hole in it. Rub some ordinary cutting oil on the surface and slowly heat it until the oil burns. Then place the article to one side and allow it to cool slowly in the air.

Discussion Topics

1. Why is it necessary to anneal and pickle nonferrous metals?
2. What does the pickling solution consist of? How is it made?
3. Must the entire article be annealed at once? Should it be heated quickly or slowly?
4. Describe the appearance of copper at annealing temperature.
5. How and when should the article be placed in the pickling solution, and how should it be removed?
6. How long should the article remain in the solution?
7. In what way is aluminum treated to make sure it will not be melted during annealing?

Unit 37. Sinking and Beating Down a Tray

You can shape shallow trays, plates, and bowls by beating the metal down into a form or block. There are three common ways: sinking rectangular plates in a vise, sinking or beating down in a wood or metal form, and beating down over a wood or metal block.

SINKING RECTANGULAR PLATES

1. Lay out and cut a piece of metal to a rectangular shape that is slightly larger than the finished size of the project.

2. Mark a line indicating the area to be sunk.

3. Cut two pieces of hardwood or angle iron to a length equal to the longest side of the metal.

4. Secure a rounded hardwood stick or metal punch and a ball-peen hammer.

5. Fasten the metal in a vise between the wood or metal jaws with the layout line just above the edge of the jaws.

6. Hold the punch just above the vise jaws and strike it firmly with the hammer. Work along from one side to the

other, sinking the metal a little at a time. Turn the metal a quarter turn and repeat. Anneal as necessary.

7. When the forming is complete, the edge will be stretched out of shape. Trim it with snips, file it, and then decorate. Frequently, either the edge or the recessed portion is planished, and sometimes both are.

BEATING DOWN A TRAY INTO A FORM

1. Select a metal or wood form with a recessed section of the desired size. For simple, small trays, the top of an electrical-outlet box can be used. It is also possible to make a form of round, oval, or irregular shape by cutting out the center of a ¾-inch piece of plywood to the desired shape and fastening the outside to another piece of plywood (Fig. 37-1). Select a forming hammer (Fig. 37-2).

2. Cut a piece of metal slightly larger than the size of the tray. Small trays can be made of 24- or 22-gauge metal, while larger ones require 20- or 18-gauge. The metal can be rectangular in shape or cut to the approximate outside shape of the finished project.

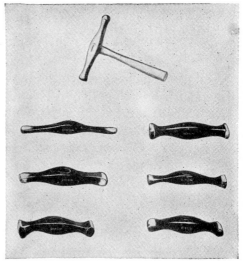

FIG. 37-2. Hammers for beating down can be of wood, plastics, or metal.

3. Lay out a line showing the section to be beaten down.

4. Hold the metal over the form or, if you wish, clamp it in place. This can be done by fastening strips of wood around the edge of the metal with C clamps.

5. Use a metal- or wood-forming hammer or a round-pointed hardwood stick and a wood mallet, and begin just

FIG. 37-3. Beating down, or sinking, a tray in a form. A metal hammer may be used.

FIG. 37-1. Some forms for beating down.

inside the layout line to strike the metal with glancing blows in order to outline the area to be sunk (Fig. 37-3).

6. After you have gone completely around the form once or twice, the metal will require annealing. (See Unit 36.)

7. Continue to form the metal. As it takes shape, work in toward the center in concentric rows until the metal is stretched to the bottom of the form. Then strike the metal angular blows to form the edge of the recess clearly.

8. If the metal is not clamped, remember to keep the edge flat by striking it with the flat of a wooden mallet (Fig. 37-4).

9. Finish the project by cutting, filing, and enriching the edge as desired.

BEATING DOWN OVER A WOOD OR METAL BLOCK

1. Select a wood or metal block, similar to that shown in Fig. 37-5, with a cutout portion that will reproduce the kind of recess you want. The advantage of using this kind of block is that any size plate can be made. If the block is

FIG. 37-5. Beating down a tray over a wooden or metal block.

wooden, fasten two pins in the top of it at a distance from the edge equal to the edge of the tray. Fasten the block in a vise with the recessed portion extending above the jaws.

2. Cut out a piece of metal to the size and shape of the tray.

3. Hold the metal firmly against the two guide pins. Use a round-nosed metal or wood hammer to strike the metal just beyond the edge of the block.

4. Move the metal slightly after each stroke of the hammer and go completely around the plate. Always keep the edge of the metal flat and anneal the project as necessary (Figs. 37-6 and 37-7). The secret of success in this kind of forming

FIG. 37-4. Flattening the edge of a tray with a wooden, rubber, or rawhide mallet.

FIG. 37-6. Flattening the edge.

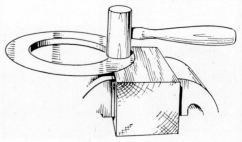

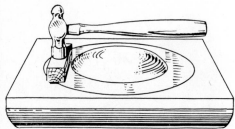

Fig. 37-7. Another method of flattening the edge.

is to get the shape started correctly the first time around.

5. As the project approaches finished shape, strike the metal with sharp, glancing blows to clearly form the recessed portion. Flatten the bottom (Fig. 37-8).

Fig. 37-8. Truing the bottom.

6. Trim the edge and decorate as desired.

Discussion Topics

1. In what three ways can metal be shaped into trays, plates, and bowls?
2. Describe the simplest method of sinking a rectangular plate.
3. Is it necessary to anneal from time to time during the forming process?
4. How can the edge be finished?
5. Small projects are usually made of what thickness of metal? Large projects?
6. Should the metal be clamped to the form?
7. What kind of hammers and mallets are needed?
8. Is it necessary to outline the beaten-down area first before beginning the forming?
9. What advantage does the use of a metal block have?
10. What is the purpose of the two guide pins?

Unit 38. Raising a Bowl

Bowls can be formed by raising the metal over simple wood forms (Figs. 38-1 and 38-2). These have the advantage of being usable for any size of bowl. A raising hammer is needed.

Raising

1. Determine the amount of material needed by bending a piece of wire to the cross-sectional shape of the bowl.

Then by stretching it out you can determine the diameter of the disk.

2. Cut a circular piece large enough for the bowl and cut to disk shape.

3. Locate the center of the disk. With a pencil compass draw several concentric circles on the disk spaced equal distances apart. These are guide lines for the forming.

4. Fasten the block in a vise with the

FIG. 38-1. A form for raising a bowl.

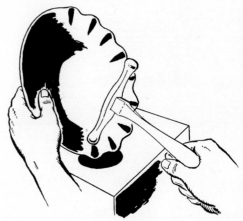

FIG. 38-3. The first step in raising a bowl. Rotate the disk slightly after each hammer blow. As the bowl takes shape, lower the angle at which it is held.

end grain up and pound or gouge out a depression in the wood.

5. Strike the metal near the edge with the raising hammer and rotate the disk

FIG. 38-2. A stake tree made from a section of log with various sizes of conical holes.

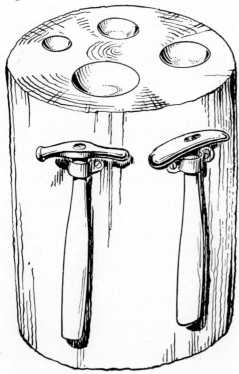

after each blow (Fig. 38-3). Make the blows uniform and overlapped. Never allow the metal to wrinkle so badly that it folds over, for this would ruin the piece. Continue to hammer around the concentric circles until the center of the disk is reached.

6. By this time the disk will be hard and will require annealing and pickling.

7. When the disk is clean, replace the concentric circles with the pencil compass.

8. Continue to stretch the metal by hammering it as you rotate the disk. As the forming proceeds, lower the disk over the depression. Do not be discouraged as the bowl will appear very crude during the forming (Fig. 38-4). At frequent intervals anneal and pickle. Continue to form the metal until the approximate shape is secured.

9. Select a metal stake of the approximate bowl curvature. Place the bowl in an inverted position over the stake, and with a wooden or rawhide mallet work

FIG. 38-4. The shape of the bowl throughout the various steps in raising.

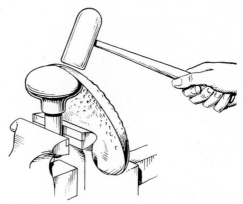

FIG. 38-6. Smoothing out the imperfections of a bowl that has been raised.

out the imperfections (Figs. 38-5 and 38-6).

10. With a surface gauge mark the edge true and then trim it with tin snips (Fig. 38-7).

11. Anneal and pickle the bowl and clean and polish it in preparation for planishing.

12. Planish the outside of the bowl with a round-faced metal stake and a planishing hammer. See the next unit, "Decorating the Surface or Edge."

13. Decorate the edge, make a base, or add appendages to finish it.

14. The early forming of the bowl can also be done over a sandbag. Fill a heavy canvas bag about two-thirds full with fine sand. Form a depression in the bag and proceed as with a wooden form (Fig. 38-8).

15. The forming can also be done by the crimping method (Fig. 38-9). Divide the disk into several equal segments and

FIG. 38-7. Using a surface-height gauge to mark a line around a bowl as a guide for trimming it evenly.

FIG. 38-5. Some common stakes that can be used to smooth out a bowl.

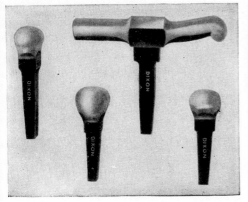

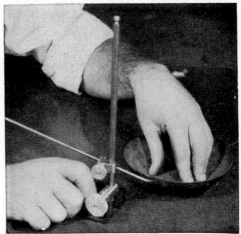

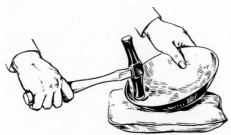

Fig. 38-8. The first stage of raising a bowl can be done over a sandbag.

then crimp the metal along these lines. Stretch the crimped disk over a stake. Repeat the crimping and stretching until the desired depth is reached.

Discussion Topics

1. What kind of stake and hammer do you need?
2. Why are circular lines laid out on the piece?
3. How can the irregularities be

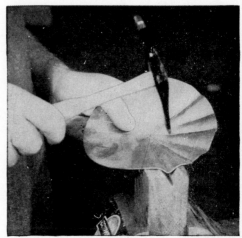

Fig. 38-9. Another method of raising a bowl is by crimping the edge over a crimping block. Notice the kind of hammer used. The edge is crimped and the bowl smoothed off over a stake.

smoothed out after the shaping is done?
4. How can the outside of the bowl be finished?

Unit 39. Decorating the Surface or Edge

There are many things that can be done to the surface or edge of a tray, plate, bowl, or dish to add to its beauty and to give it a distinctive appearance (Fig. 39-3).

PLANISHING

Planishing gives a smooth, even texture to the surface of metal. It is similar to peening, as described in Unit 16, in "Decorating the Surface and Ends of Metal," page 62, except that planishing hammers and stakes are used when available (Figs. 39-1 and 39-2). Planishing removes blemishes, bruises and ir-

regularities that have developed during the forming. On deep dishes or bowls the outside surface is planished, but on shallow trays or plates the upper surface, or frequently only the edge, is decorated.

PLANISHING A DEEP BOWL OR DISH

1. Select a good planishing hammer and a round-faced stake that has about the same curvature as the bowl. Both should be free of nicks and scratches. Fasten the stake in a vise.

2. Draw a few concentric pencil lines around the outside of the bowl to guide in the work.

Fig. 39-1. Planishing stakes.

Fig. 39-3. Planishing a flat bracelet.

3. Hold the bowl over the stake with your fingers underneath and your thumb on top to guide it and to hold it securely. Keep your elbow close to your body and operate the hammer with uniform wrist movement. When done correctly, the hammering will produce a clear ring as the hammer strikes the metal. If it is not done correctly, you will hear a dull thud.

4. Begin to planish the surface at the center, and do one area at a time, moving the article slightly after each blow (Fig. 39-5). Keep the stroke uniform and slightly overlap the blows. Rub the surface with fine abrasive cloth to highlight the areas that have been planished. Work from the center outward, follow-

ing the concentric circles. The beginner frequently strikes the metal too hard and too irregularly.

PLANISHING TRAYS OR DISHES

1. Support the surface to be planished over solid metal or over a lead block. Frequently the article can remain in the metal form used to shape it (Figs. 39-4, 39-5, and 39-6).

2. Planish as described above.

LAYOUT FOR EDGE DECORATION

To lay out the position for flutes, domes, scallops, flaring, or for other spaced decorations, proceed as follows:

1. Cut a disk of paper the same size

Fig. 39-2. Planishing hammers.

Fig. 39-4. Planishing an edge.

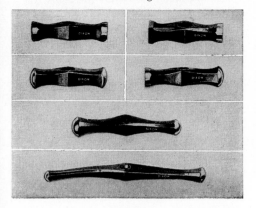

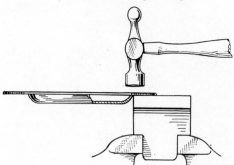

FIG. 39-5. Planishing a bowl.

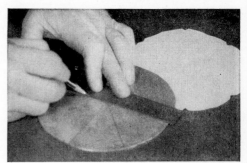

FIG. 39-7. A method of dividing an object into equal parts by folding a piece of paper, clipping the corners, and using it as a pattern.

as the project. Fold the paper into the number of segments in the design.

2. Clip the corners of the folded paper, open it up, and lay it on the metal. Mark the position for the decorations with a pencil or chalk (Fig. 39-7). If necessary, draw a line from the edge to the center, and locate the exact position of the area to be decorated. This

FIG. 39-6. Planishing a shallow tray over a lead block.

can also be done by trial and error with the dividers.

SHAPING AN EDGE

After a bowl or tray has been shaped and planished, the edge should be cut to finished size, filed, and smoothed with abrasive cloth. In addition, you may enrich the edge by filing recesses in it at regular intervals. Strike the edge at right angles with a dull chisel to raise or to shape it, or add other decorations to beautify the edge.

DOMING

A *dome* is a raised, conical shape, frequently placed at equal intervals, or in groups, around the edge of an object.

Method 1. Cut or gouge a small conical shape in a wood block and then hold the face surface of the object over this. Strike the back of the metal at the layout position with a ball-peen hammer or with a round-faced punch.

Method 2. Cut a piece of pipe that has an inside opening equal to the diameter of the dome. Round the inner edge of the pipe. Select a ball-peen hammer that

FIG. 39-10. Forms for fluting the edge of a bowl.

FIG. 39-8. Dapping block and punches. These are used to form small conical shapes in all kinds of objects, such as along the edge of a bowl or tray or on a bracelet.

will fit part way into the pipe. Fasten the pipe in a vise. Hold the article over the pipe, place the ball-peen hammer in position, and strike it with another hammer.

Method 3. Dapping blocks and punches (Fig. 39-8) are available for this kind of decoration. These punches and blocks are also used for making half a sphere, which can be soldered to another half to make balls.

FLUTING

A *flute* is a long, narrow indentation. To flute the edge of a flat plate, secure a

soft piece of wood and a metal rod of the diameter of the flute. Place the rod over the wood and strike it several times to form the depression. Then place the edge of the plate over the wood with the metal rod over it. Strike the rod several times, forming the flute (Fig. 39-9).

On a curved dish first cut a wood form that fits the shape of the curve (Fig. 39-10). Gouge out the shape of the flute. Hold the dish over the form and pound in the flutes with a ball-peen or forming hammer.

SCALLOPING

To scallop the edge of a dish, use a wood jig (Fig. 39-11). Slip the metal between the opening in the jig and bend (Fig. 39-12). This can also be done with a round-jaw pliers that has been heavily taped with masking tape.

FIG. 39-9. Fluting the flat edge of a tray.

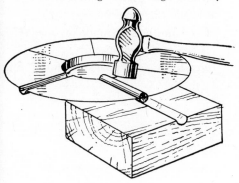

FIG. 39-11. A simple jig for scalloping the edge of a plate.

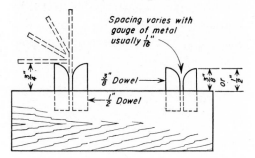

Spacing varies with gauge of metal usually $\frac{1}{8}$"

$\frac{3}{8}$" Dowel

$\frac{1}{2}$" Dowel

Fig. 39-12. Using a commercial-type bending jig for scalloping.

FLARING

Flaring is turning the very edge of metal slightly. On dishes and bowls the flaring should be done over a hardwood block that has a slightly rounded corner. Hold the article over the block and strike it with a round-faced wooden or rawhide mallet. To flare the end of tubing, fasten it in a simple wood jig and clamp this in a vise. Then place the head of a ball-peen hammer that is slightly larger than the diameter of the tubing in the end of the tubing, and strike the ball-peen hammer with another hammer (Fig. 39-13).

OVERLAYING

Cut a piece of decorative wire long enough to go around the edge of a plate or bowl. Form it into shape and then sweat-solder it in place.

The surface can also be decorated by cutting out a design in a contrasting metal and sweat-soldering this in position.

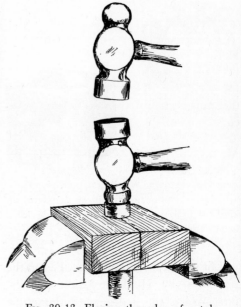

Fig. 39-13. Flaring the edge of a tube.

Discussion Topics

1. What is "planishing"? How does it differ from "peening"?
2. What kind of stakes are needed for planishing?
3. How can you tell if you are handling the hammer correctly?
4. In what ways can an edge be shaped to decorate it?
5. What is a simple way of laying out a decoration that is to be repeated around the edge?
6. What is "doming"?
7. How can flutes be made in an edge?
8. How is scalloping done?
9. On what type of project would flaring be done?

Unit 40. Etching a Design

Etching a design is an interesting process because it is fascinating to watch the design take shape as the chemical eats away the metal. Etching is quite easy to do, but the important thing is to cover carefully the area of the design that is not to be etched (Figs. 40-1 and 40-2).

MATERIALS

The materials used to cover the protected part of the metal are called *resists*. For simple etching in which only lines are cut, beeswax is good. For more complicated patterns asphaltum varnish or acid-resist enamel applied with a good camel's-hair brush is excellent. For straight pattern work the metal can be covered with masking tape and the area to be affected cut away with a sharp knife.

For etching copper, brass, and pewter, a solution of one part nitric acid to one part water is needed. Remember: mix the acid into the water in a glass or earthenware jar. For aluminum combine one part muriatic (hydrochloric) acid and one part water.

ETCHING

1. The surface of the metal must be perfectly clean. Either clean it in an acid bath (pickling) or use fine abrasives (Fig. 40-3). After the metal is clean, do not touch it. Failure to observe this rule is one of the major causes of poor etching.

2. Apply the resist by one of the following methods:

   a. Masking-tape method. Cover the article with masking tape and lay out or transfer the design to this paper surface. Cut around the area to be exposed with a sharp knife, carefully lifting off the tape from this section.

   b. Asphaltum-varnish method. Carefully transfer the pattern to the metal by tracing with carbon paper. Paint on the asphaltum on the areas that are not to be affected by the acid (Fig. 40-4). If the piece is flat or if the entire article must be put into the acid bath, both surfaces must be covered with the varnish. The edges, in this case, require special attention

FIG. 40-1. A group of etched bracelets and pins showing the attractive projects that can be made by the etching method.

FIG. 40-2. A handsome, etched plate.

FIG. 40-3. The materials needed for etching—including the asphaltum varnish, the acid, the piece of metal, and the cleaning materials: steel wool, scouring powder, and fine oil. Notice the jig for scalloping the edge in the lower left-hand corner (see Fig. 39-12).

and should be given two or three coats. If you are etching a tray or bowl, however, only the front surface requires treatment, and the acid can be poured into it. Be sure to apply enough resist. The area should appear black. Allow it to dry for 24 hours.

3. Insert the article in the acid or pour the acid solution into the article. The exact time needed for etching will vary with the strength of the acid and the depth of etching desired. The approximate time is 1 hour for copper, $1\frac{1}{2}$ for

FIG. 40-4. Applying the asphaltum varnish with a camel's-hair brush. Note that the varnish is being applied to the design in this case so the background will be etched. The reverse could also be done.

FIG. 40-5. Applying the acid. A stick with cotton wrapped around it is used to keep the acid moving. This is especially important when a small amount is poured into a tray. Articles, such as bracelets or pins, are coated on the back side also, since they are immersed in the etching solution.

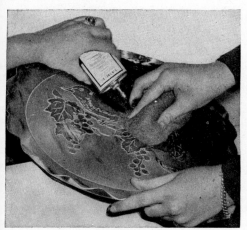

FIG. 40-6. Cleaning off the asphaltum after the etching is completed.

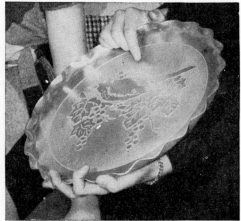

FIG. 40-7. You, too, would be proud of a project as handsome as this one.

brass, $\frac{1}{4}$ for pewter, and $\frac{1}{2}$ for aluminum. Stir the acid during the etching with a narrow wooden stick wrapped in cotton (Fig. 40-5).

4. Take the article from the solution and then remove the resist. If asphaltum is used, clean with benzine or with gasoline.

5. Polish the tray with steel wool and fine oil (Figs. 40-6 and 40-7).

6. Check your work. Is the design clearly outlined? Is the edge ragged? This would be caused by too rapid action or by a poorly applied resist.

Discussion Topics

1. Describe the process of etching a design on metal.
2. What is the etching agent? What is "resist"? How is it applied?
3. Can the same etching solution be used for all metals?
4. Why is it necessary to clean the metal thoroughly?
5. How is the pattern transferred to the metal?
6. Does the actual etching time vary with the kind of metal?

Unit 41. Doing Wire Work

Many art-metal and jewelry projects have wire parts. A few pointers on how to handle wire will therefore be helpful.

TWISTING WIRE

If a twisted wire for a decorative edge or overlay is needed, cut a piece that is a little more than twice as long as the finished length. Clamp the two open ends together in a vise. Place a small metal rod through the closed end and draw it tight. Turn the rod to twist the wire the desired amount. If the proper amount of pressure is applied, the wire will remain

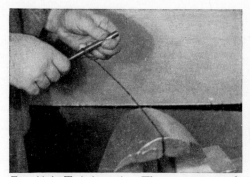

Fig. 41-1. Twisting wire. The two open ends are clamped in the vise, a rod placed in the closed end, and the two wires twisted together.

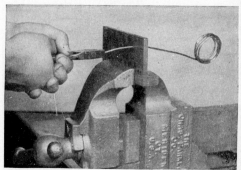

Fig. 41-2. Drawing wire. A method of changing the shape of wire or of reducing its size by drawing through a drawplate.

straight, and the twists will be even and uniform (Fig. 41-1).

After the double wire has been twisted, it is sometimes flattened with a metal hammer to lock the two wires together and to provide a flat surface for making bracelets and rings.

To twist wires of different shape:

1. Fasten the ends together in a metal vise.

2. Hold the two wires between your thumb and forefinger, and twist as you draw your hand away from the vise.

DRAWING WIRE

To change the shape or size of wire, pull it through a *draw plate* with *draw tongs*. In most cases, No. 18-gauge wire of each different kind of metal is purchased, and then, from this size, many different sizes and shapes can be made. To reduce the size or to change the shape of wire:

1. Grind or file one end to a point and anneal the wire.

2. Fasten the drawplate in a vise.

Apply wax or soap to the wire as a lubricant.

3. Insert the wire in one of the holes that is slightly smaller than the wire size. Draw it through (Fig. 41-2).

4. Insert the wire in the next smaller hole and repeat. Continue this until the desired size is obtained.

The wire will require annealing from time to time. Do not attempt to reduce the wire size too rapidly or jerk it through the drawplate too fast.

MAKING SMALL TUBING

1. Cut a strip of metal that is three times as wide as the diameter of the tubing and as long as is desired.

2. Taper one end of the strip.

3. Hold the tapered end over a grooved block and with a cross-peen hammer form the section into a V shape.

4. Lock the drawplate in the vise. Insert the tapered section in a hole larger than the tubing and draw it through. Continue to draw it through smaller holes until the tubing is formed.

1. How can wire be twisted?
2. What tool is needed to change the size or shape of wire?
3. Must the wire be annealed?

4. Can the wire be drawn in one step? Explain.
5. Describe the process of making small tubing.

Unit 42. Hard-soldering a Joint

Hard-soldering is similar to brazing (See Unit 52, "Gas or Oxyacetylene Welding and Brazing," page 175.) and always requires a high degree of heat. Usually objects of copper, brass, or silver are hard-soldered since the joint is neater and more permanent than when they are soft-soldered.

Soldering Tools and Materials

It is important to have a good source of heat for hard-soldering. If city gas is available, a *gas torch* or *blow pipe* with air from a foot bellows or air compressor is good (Figs. 42-1 and 42-2). A *bunsen*

burner with a mouth-type blowpipe (Fig. 42-3) or an *oxyacetylene welding outfit* is also excellent.

Silver solder can be purchased in three grades: (1) easy or low-melting, which becomes fluid at 1325°F and is used only when a single joint is to be made; (2) medium, which melts at 1390°F for use on the first joint when two joints are to be made; and (3) hard, melting at 1400°F for use on the best type joint. Some idea of these melting points can be gained from the heat colors: 900F— just-visible red; 1200°F—dull red; and 1400°F—cherry red.

Fig. 42-1. A blowpipe for gas and a foot bellows.

Fig. 42-2. A blowpipe with gas and air from a compressor.

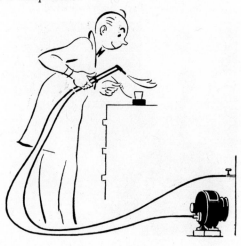

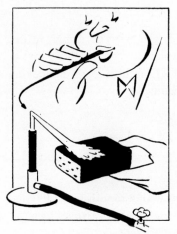

Fig. 42-3. A bunsen burner and a blowpipe for soldering.

A flux can be either borax and water in paste form or, better still, a commercial paste flux. Solder in paste form that combines both the solder and flux can also be purchased.

Soldering

1. Solder will not stick to metal that is covered with oxide, dirt, or grease; so clean the joint with a file, knife, or abra-

Fig. 42-4. A method of wiring the sides to the bottom of the box that is to be soldered.

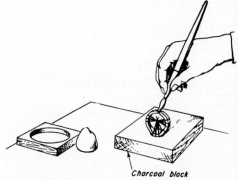

Fig. 42-5. Applying the flux to the joint with a camel's-hair brush. Note that the ring is wired together so that the joint will not open up when the heat is applied.

sive cloth. It is a good idea to file a slight V at the joint for the solder to flow into.

2. Fit the pieces perfectly, and bind them together with black iron oxide wire to keep them from springing apart when the heat is applied. Figure 42-4 shows a successful way of wiring a box, and Fig. 42-5 shows a ring wired for soldering. Place the work over a charcoal block, and also put a block of charcoal or a piece of asbestos back of the object to reflect the heat.

3. Flatten the solder if necessary and cut it into tiny squares or pellets on a piece of clean paper (Fig. 42-6). Mix a borax-and-water flux to a creamy paste and paint it on the joint with a small

Fig. 42-6. Cutting small bits of silver solder.

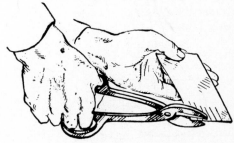

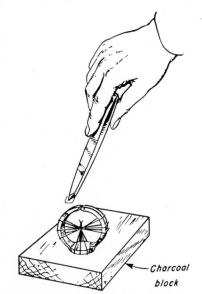

FIG. 42-7. Using a tweezers to place the small bits of solder on the joint.

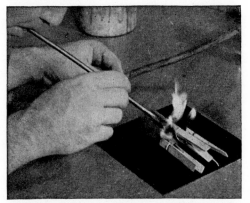

FIG. 42-8. Soldering. The piece is held in place with spring-type clothespins.

camel's-hair brush. Mix and apply commercial flux the same way (Fig. 42-5).

4. Carefully apply the small bits of solder along the joint with tweezers, using slightly more solder than is necessary to fill the joint (Fig. 42-7). The flux brush is also handy for picking up the small pieces of solder.

5. Bring the blue part of the flame up to the joint and preheat the area until the flux dries out. This will hold the solder in place (Figs. 42-8 and 42-9).

6. Bring the inner point of the flame up to the joint, and heat to the correct temperature as guided by the heat colors. If possible, heat the joint from the back side and avoid putting the heat directly on the solder. It is important to get the soldering done quickly. Do not hold the flame on the article too long. When the solder melts, it will flow or run fast. Remove the heat immediately. If pieces of different size or thickness are being joined, apply most of the heat to the thicker piece.

7. Place the article in a pickling solution to remove the oxide and then rinse with water.

8. Check your work. If the solder rolls into balls or pellets and does not join, the work is not clean or there is not enough heat; the solder is being heated and not the joint. If the joint melts away or the silver burns and smokes, the flame is too hot.

FIG. 42-9. Sometimes a shield must be placed around the object to concentrate the heat.

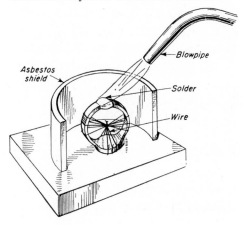

Discussion Topics

1. What type of projects usually requires hard-soldering?
2. How is the high degree of heat obtained?
3. What is "hard solder"?
4. Is a flux required?
5. Why is it necessary to bind the joint together?

6. Explain how the heat is applied. Do you apply the flame directly to the solder?
7. How do you know when to remove the heat?
8. What is wrong if the solder rolls into balls and does not run?

Unit 43. Polishing, Coloring, and Preserving

The finish on a project should add to its beauty and bring out its best qualities. This is especially true of projects that are made of the art metals: copper, brass, nickel silver, aluminum, and silver.

POLISHING MATERIALS

All small scratches and imperfections must be removed first by buffing or with abrasive cloth. A *power buffer,* either bench or hand type, is desirable for polishing, or a *polishing wheel* can be fastened to a lathe or drill press. These wheels are made of cotton, flannel, or felt and are sewn together at the center with a soft outer edge. Always have several wheels, one for each different polishing compound.

The four materials most commonly used are tripoli or pumice for first polishing and rouge or whiting to obtain a very highly burnished surface.

POLISHING

1. Mount the wheels on the buffing head or other power machine. Hold the stick of polishing compound lightly against the outer surface of the wheel as it is revolving (Fig. 43-1).

2. Hold the project lightly against the wheel and work it back and forth (Fig. 43-2). Apply additional polishing compound to the wheel as needed. Wipe the project clean.

3. Change to another wheel and finer compound to complete the polishing.

4. Wash the project in hot water and dry with a clean cloth or in sawdust. Do not touch it with your hands.

5. For a high luster it should imme-

FIG. 43-1. Always apply the polishing compound to the edge of a soft wheel.

FIG. 43-2. For polishing, hold the project lightly against the edge of the wheel.

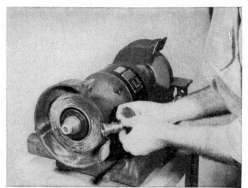

FIG. 43-3. For a satin finish, a wire brush may be installed on the grinder.

diately be coated with lacquer, plastic, or wax.

SATIN FINISH

Satin finish can be applied to metal by holding the project against a revolving wire brush (Fig. 43-3).

HAND POLISHING

If power equipment is not available, the polishing can be done by hand by first rubbing the project with crocus cloth and then polishing with a chamois dipped in rouge.

COLORING

To add interest to the metal surface or to produce a surface that has light and dark tones, you can color metals with chemicals. The one most commonly used on brass, copper, and silver is *liver of sulfur*.

Apply liver of sulfur as follows:

1. Dissolve a piece of liver of sulfur about the size of a small marble in a gallon of hot water.

2. Be sure that the article is clean. If necessary, scrub with pumice and water.

3. Dip the article until the proper color is obtained, from brown to black on copper or brass and black on silver.

4. Hand-polish to high-light certain areas, or allow the article to remain all one tone. Usually in silver work the crevices are left black and the rest high-lighted.

PRESERVING

All metals oxidize or discolor if exposed to the air. Metals such as pewter and aluminum discolor very little, but others such as brass and copper oxidize a great deal. Most metals, therefore, should be protected by some preservative such as *wax, clear lacquer,* or *plastic*. Wax is a temporary finish; it is applied with a soft cloth, allowed to dry, and then rubbed briskly. Clear metal lacquer is the preferred covering. First, heat the article slightly, keeping the fingers away from the clean metal surface, and then apply the lacquer with a good camel's-hair brush. The lacquer must be applied very sparingly to keep it from running. Cover one area at a time and do not go over the surface again. Small articles can be dipped in lacquer. Be sure to clean the brush with lacquer thinner. Clear plastic and lacquer can be obtained in pressurized cans and applied in a fine spray.

Discussion Topics

1. Why are metals polished?
2. What kind of equipment can be used for machine polishing?

3. Name the polishing compounds. How are they applied to the wheel?
4. Can a complete polishing job be done with one grade of polishing compound?
5. Should the project be coated, after polishing, to preserve the finish?
6. What coloring material is most often used on brass, copper, and silver?

Unit 44. Metal Spinning

The art of metal spinning is centuries old but is still practiced today both as a hobby and as a commercial method of shaping metal. Metal spinning is shaping a flat disk over a form into plates, bowls, and other similar shapes. In the manufacture of limited numbers of a single article, spinning is the preferred method since this is less expensive than shaping by drawing between dies (Fig. 44-1). Although the process of spinning can be very complicated and can use up a great deal of metal in a short time, the beginner is able to learn the fundamentals

and to turn out attractive coasters, dishes, trays, and bowls (Fig. 44-2).

EQUIPMENT, TOOLS, AND MATERIALS

You will need a sturdy *wood or metal lathe* with end-thrust bearings in the headstock (Fig. 44-3). The tailstock must be equipped with a follower and follower block, and a tool rest designed

Fig. 44-2. The kind of projects that can best be done by spinning.

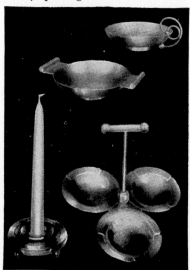

Fig. 44-1. Here you see a commercial spinner shaping a base for a table lamp over a wooden form.

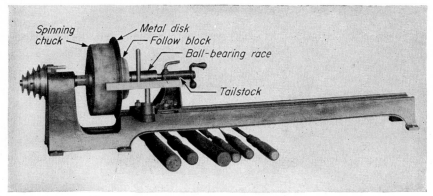

FIG. 44-3. A metal spinning lathe.

for spinning is also necessary (Fig. 44-4).

The *spinning tools* (Figs. 44-4 and 44-5) are relatively easy to make from discarded wood-turning tools. You need a back stick, that can be made from a piece of 1½- by 1½- by 24-inch hardwood, tapered at one end to a chisel shape. The chuck, or forms, can be made of metal or wood; you may choose oak, maple, or cherry (Fig. 44-6). The chucks should always be made slightly longer than the article so that when they are fitted to the headstock spindle there will be space in which the tool can trim the object to finished size.

Spinning metals are copper, brass, aluminum, pewter, sterling silver, and a special type of steel. When spinning copper or brass, you must always keep the metal soft, for it hardens rapidly during the shaping and will crack if not annealed.

FIG. 44-5. Spinning tools: (*a*) flat tool; (*b*) pointed tool; (*c*) cutoff tool; (*d*) beading tool; (*e*) ball tool.

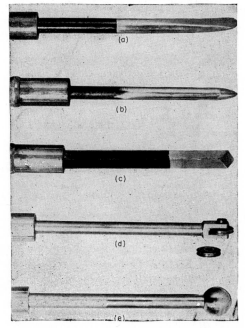

FIG. 44-4. Top, left to right: a spinning center to which the follower block is fastened, a tool rest, and a spinning-face plate. Bottom: a typical tool for spinning.

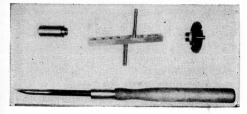

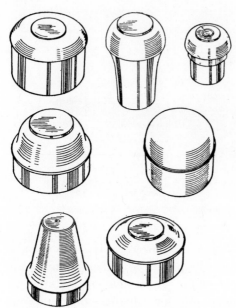

FIG. 44-6. Typical shapes of wood chucks.

FIG. 44-7. Spinning a small bowl.

A *lubricant* of tallow oil or yellow laundry soap must be ready for lubricating the metal as it is spun.

SPINNING A SIMPLE BOWL

1. Fasten a wood chuck to the headstock spindle and attach the follower block in the tailstock.

2. Cut a disk of soft metal to the approximate diameter needed to form the project.

3. Insert the disk between the chuck and the follower block and turn up the pressure slightly on the tailstock to hold it in position.

4. As you turn the lathe over by hand, tap the disk first from one side and then from the other until it runs true. You can also make it run true by turning the power on and holding the end of the back stick lightly against the edge of the disk. This is more dangerous, however, and requires that the lathe be adjusted to

the slowest possible speed. When the disk runs true, tighten the tailstock to hold the metal firmly in place.

5. Adjust the tool rest about $1\frac{1}{2}$ to 2 inches away from the edge of the disk. It should be possible to insert the fulcrum pin at any point along the total length of the chuck. Also adjust the spindle speed to about 900 to 1,200 revolutions per minute (rpm). Place the fulcrum pin about 1 inch ahead of the disk.

6. Turn on the power. *Never stand directly back of the disk;* this is the time that it could fly out and strike you. Apply a little tallow or yellow laundry soap to both surfaces of the disk to lubricate.

7. Select a flat tool, and hold the handle under your right arm, grasping the tool with your right hand toward the front of the handle.

8. Hold the blade of the tool firmly against the fulcrum pin, as shown in Fig. 44-7, with the rounded side of the tool against the disk at and slightly below the center. Now apply pressure, moving the point of the tool down and to the left as you move the handle to the right to seat the metal against the chuck. When this happens, the metal may tend to dish out and wrinkle slightly. Insert a second fulcrum pin ahead of the disk. Now hold

the point of the back stick against the front of the disk opposite the flat tool which is against the back (Fig. 44-1). Straighten out the disk until it is funnel-shaped. Always keep the unformed part of the disk to this shape. It may be desirable at this stage to trim the edge of the disk with the cutoff tool.

9. Move the fulcrum pin to the next hole, and use the rounded part of your flat tool to shape the metal against the chuck. Always keep the point of the tool that meets the metal moving back and forth in an arc of about 2 inches. If you force the metal in only one direction, it will thin out very rapidly and crack open at this point. Also, never allow the point of the tool to rest on the metal any length of time as this will form ridges. Always be careful to keep the edge from dishing out or becoming wrinkled. On shallow dishes the spinning can be done rapidly and can be completed before the metal becomes hard. If a deeper dish is being formed, anneal the metal at this stage.

10. Replace the dish and re-lubricate both surfaces. Move the fulcrum pin nearer the headstock. Remember: always have the pin in such a position that you are forming the metal about an inch on either side of its location. Use the back stick whenever necessary to straighten out the metal to funnel shape. Work the metal in the curves and around the corners.

11. Before the last portion of the dish is spun, trim the edge again; then work the rest of the dish down against the form.

12. If a double edge is desired on the dish, hold the back stick against the left edge of the disk while the flat tool is held against the right side. Force the edge up at right angles. Then hold a beading tool against the left side of the turned-up edge to force over and form a rounded edge.

13. Polish the outside of the project and remove it from the chuck.

Discussion Topics

1. Explain the process of metal spinning.
2. On what kind of machine is it done? What tools are needed?
3. Which metals are most commonly selected?
4. Is it necessary to anneal during the spinning process?
5. Is a lubricant necessary?
6. Since this is a fairly dangerous operation, what precautions should be taken?

Section V. FORGING

Unit 45. Introduction to Forging

In forging, you will try your skill at a trade as old as civilized man, that of blacksmithing. In hand forging, the metal is heated in a forge and shaped over an anvil with various kinds of hammers and tools. In production work many types of large presses and drop hammers are employed. The metal is heated and then is either forged to shape in dies or in a free-hand manner under heavy pounding. Although the old-time blacksmith who makes repairs and forms small tools by hand-forge methods practices a trade that has greatly decreased, power forging has increased.

A closely allied field is that of the ornamental-iron worker who makes wrought-iron or aluminum decorations for buildings and homes. He, too, must heat and shape his metal into artistic designs. Of the various ways in which metal can be shaped, forging is most useful for parts which must have great strength and be subject to stress, for example, for crankshafts, axles, gun barrels, and other heavy parts of machinery. In production work the metal is heated to working temperature by men called *heaters,* and then the hot metal is shaped in one of a variety of machines (Fig. 45-1). If many articles of the same shape are to be made, dies are used into which

the heated metal is stamped by a large press or drop hammer. Of course, the article must go through several stages of forming and cannot be shaped all at one time (Fig. 45-2).

Other types of forgings are made by machines that squeeze the hot metal into shape. When unusual-shaped articles must be forged, the work is done on a power hammer in which there are no dies. This operation is the most skilled type of forging and is done by men called *hammersmiths.* It is fascinating to watch these men shape a large part merely by skillfully moving the hot metal under the blows of the hammers.

Blacksmiths, whose work is all hand forging, are needed in our modern industrial world for maintenance jobs on buildings and on road construction and for operating small repair shops, in which forging is only one of many skills they must possess. There are over 100,000 men employed in hand and machine forging in the United States, of which less than 9,000 are blacksmiths.

Ornamental-iron workers, who number about 25,000, must be highly skilled both in design and in hand forging (Fig. 45-3).

Most of the machine forging is done in large production plants near industrial

146.

Fig. 45-1. This huge steam drop hammer is forging out crankshafts for automobile engines.

Fig. 45-3. This beautiful wrought-aluminum entrance gate is an example of fine work.

centers, principally in Michigan and Illinois. Most forgings are made of steel, but brass, bronze, copper, and aluminum are also shaped in this manner. To be really proficient in ornamental- or wrought-iron work as a hobby, you must be able to do hand forging.

Discussion Topics

1. What effect does forging have on the metal?
2. What is the difference between the work of the blacksmith and modern-production forging?
3. Name some of the machines used in production forging.
4. Why must hammersmiths be so highly skilled?
5. What are the chief forging metals?
6. Name the occupations in this area.

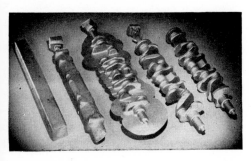

Fig. 45-2. The four stages in forging the crankshaft from a piece of steel to the finished forging. A set of dies is needed for the first and second stages. The excess metal must be trimmed for the third stage and the ends trimmed in the fourth. The forging requires machining and heat-treating before it can be used.

Unit 46. Hand Forging

Frequently the metalsmith must do simple hand forging in making repairs to metal parts for the home, farm, or shop and in making tools such as cold chisels and center punches. When making large ornamental-iron projects, a forge will be needed.

EQUIPMENT

1. The *forge* may be a small gas- or oil-fired furnace (Fig. 46-1) or the typical coal forge (Fig. 46-2). If the forge is coal, blacksmith coal is needed for fuel.

2. A blacksmith *anvil* weighs about 250 pounds (Fig. 46-3). One end of the anvil, called the *horn,* is for shaping

FIG. 46-1. A small bench gas-forging furnace.

FIG. 46-2. A coal forge. Notice the hand-operated blower. A small motor is sometimes added to make it a power blower.

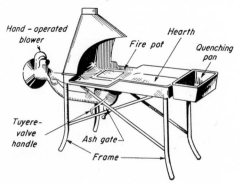

metal parts that are circular. The body of the anvil is made of cast iron or of cast steel. The face, which is made of hardened steel, is welded on and is used for all heavy pounding. The large square hole is called the *hardy hole.* Various anvil tools for shaping metal fit this hole. It is important that the anvil be solidly mounted so that it will be a sturdy base for forming the metal.

3. If a considerable amount of forging is to be done, *anvil tools* and *set hammers* should be obtained (Fig. 46-4). These tools are: bottom and top fuller for spreading and stretching metals, bottom and top swage for shaping metals, hot and cold chisels and hardies for cutting off metal, flatter for tapering and smoothing metals.

4. Variously shaped *hammers* are needed to do the forging work; some of these are shown in Fig. 46-5.

5. *Tongs* to hold the hot metal should be similar to those pictured in Fig. 46-6.

BUILDING A FORGE FIRE

1. *Gas or oil.* Light a piece of paper and place it in the furnace. Turn on a small supply of fuel until the furnace

FIG. 46-3. An anvil.

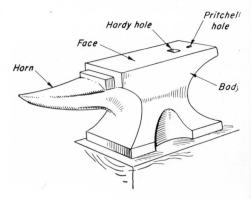

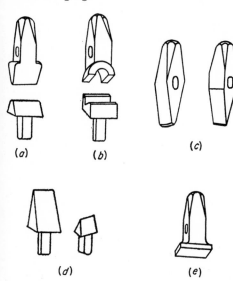

FIG. 46-4. Anvil tools: (*a*) top and bottom fuller; (*b*) top and bottom swage; (*c*) chisels; (*d*) hardies; (*e*) flatter.

lights and heats up for awhile. Then turn on an additional supply of fuel and air. Adjust the furnace until it burns with a blue or neutral flame. Too much air will cause oxidization, with the result that a heavy scale will form on the metal.

2. *Coal fire*

a. Clean out the center of the old fire, removing all the clinkers and ashes. Save some of the coke that remains from the green coal after the

FIG. 46-5. Common hammer heads: (*a*) ball peen; (*b*) cross peen; (*c*) straight peen; (*d*) sledge.

(*a*)   (*b*)   (*c*)   (*d*)

volatile gases have burned out. This will be found just outside the clinker and ash area.

b. Place a little wood shavings over the tuyere and light it. Turn on a small amount of air, using either the hand or power blower. Add some coke to the fire to build up its size.

c. After the fire gets started, pack wet, green coal around all sides of the fire except the front. As the fire burns, add more wet coal to the outside. It is extremely important to keep the forge fire adjusted for a neutral or non-oxidizing fire by controlling the amount of air. Do not apply too much air to the fire.

d. When placing metal in the fire, always insert it in the center in a horizontal position. Never thrust the metal in from the top with one end at the bottom of the fire. This would heat the piece unevenly. Remove the stock at intervals to see how hot it is. It is very easy to burn it.

FIG. 46-6. Tongs: (*a*) flat lip; (*b*) curved lip; (*c*) pickup.

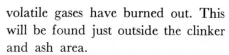

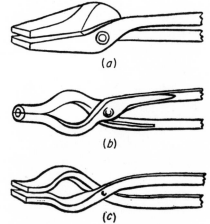

(*a*)

(*b*)

(*c*)

FORGING

For all hand forging it is important that the metal be brought to the correct temperature before shaping it. The most common metals are wrought iron, mild steel, and tool steel. Wrought iron and mild steel should be brought to a bright yellow heat before the operation is performed. Tool steel, on the other hand, should be kept to a cherry red or below. Never allow the metal to become so hot that sparks fly from it.

1. *Tapering* is done when making cold chisels or center punches and when shaping the ends of many wrought-iron projects.

    a. Heat the area of the metal to be shaped to the desired temperature. This is indicated by the color.

    b. Grasp the opposite end firmly with the tongs, and hold the heated section on the face of the anvil at an

FIG. 46-7. The helper is holding a flatter while the blacksmith strikes it to smooth out a tapered cold chisel.

angle equal to about half the desired amount of taper.

    c. Strike the heated portion with the flat of the hammer to taper it. If it is a rectangular shape, turn it a quarter turn after the first two sides are tapered. Use sharp, firm blows to do the shaping and always keep the metal at forging temperature. If round stock is being tapered, turn the stock slightly after each hammer blow.

    d. Re-heat the metal to a dull red heat and then with light hammer blows smooth out the tapered portion. If a rectangular shape is being tapered, have a helper hold a flatter against the tapered portion as you strike this tool to smooth out the taper (Fig. 46-7).

2. *Drawing out* is done to lengthen a piece of stock as the area is reduced. Figure 46-8 shows a typical piece of round stock in the various steps of being drawn out:

    a. Heat the area to the desired forging temperature.

    b. Hammer out the section to a square shape.

    c. Re-heat the metal and make an octagon shape out of it.

    d. Proceed to round off the section by striking the metal firmly as the

FIG. 46-8. The steps in drawing out a round bar to a smaller diameter: (*a*) original size; (*b*) hammering to square; (*c*) hammering to octagonal shape; (*d*) hammering again to round.

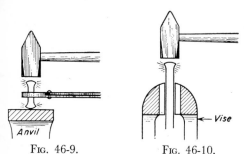

FIG. 46-9.   FIG. 46-10.

FIG. 46-9. Upsetting both ends of a short piece of stock.

FIG. 46-10. Placing the bar or rod in a vise to do the upsetting.

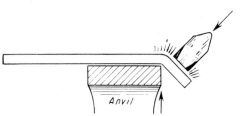

FIG. 46-12. Making an angular bend.

stock is rotated on the anvil face. If square stock is being drawn out, round it off first before attempting to proceed. This is necessary, for if the square shape is maintained during the drawing process, there is a tendency to crack the metal.

3. *Upsetting* is the opposite of drawing out. It is increasing the area of the metal by decreasing its length.

   a. Heat the section to the proper temperature.

   b. If it is a short piece, hold it on end on the anvil, and then strike the end to flatten it out. If the metal tends to bend, straighten it out by striking it as it lies flat on the anvil (Fig. 46-9).

   c. If the end of a long piece is to be enlarged, heat this area and fasten the metal in a vise with the heated end ex-

tending beyond the vise jaws. Strike the end with a hammer to increase the size. This can also be done by holding the stock with tongs on the face of the anvil with the heated end extended (Figs. 46-10 and 46-11).

4. *Bending, twisting, and flaring.* All of the operations performed on thin metal in making wrought-iron projects can be done in the same general manner on heavier stock after it has been heated. To make a sharp angle bend, for example, heat only the area of the bend. Place the stock flat on the anvil with the heated section over the edge. Strike the extended portion glancing blows with a hammer, and, finally, square off the bend over the corner of the anvil (Fig. 46-12). This can also be done by placing the metal in the vise with the bend line at the upper

FIG. 46-11. Holding the bar with tongs to upset one end as it is held flat on an anvil.

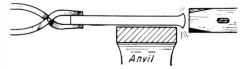

FIG. 46-13. Making a circular bend.

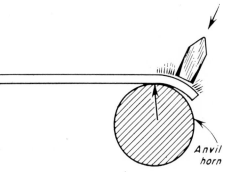

edge of the jaws. Curved shapes can be formed over the horn of the anvil (Fig. 46-13). Check the type of bending, twisting, or scrollwork that you wish to do as it is described in Section II, "Bench Metal and Wrought Iron," pages 55 to 61. Heat the metal to the desired temperature and proceed as described.

Discussion Topics

1. Describe the forging equipment.
2. How do you build a coal-forge fire?
3. Describe the proper heat for forging.
4. Tell how to insert a piece of metal into the fire.
5. What are the various operations that can be done in hand forging?

Section VI. HEAT-TREATING

Unit 47. Introduction to Heat-treating

If you have machined a center punch, forged out a cold chisel, or made any other small tools, you have found that they are useless until they are heat-treated. Heat-treating, then, is the method of conditioning metal by heating and cooling to give it the desirable properties (hardness, toughness, etc.) to do its job. All tools and a great many parts that go into machinery are worthless until they go through the heat-treating rooms.

Steels that have from medium to high carbon content (30 to 105 points) can be treated in three ways:

1. *Annealing* is a process of softening the metal to remove stresses and strains due to rolling, forging, and drawing. To anneal steel, heat it to a very high temperature, about 1475°F, and then cool it slowly. See Table 47-1 for colors and temperatures.

2. *Hardening* is a process of making the steel hard and brittle by heating it to a high temperature (1550°F for S.A.E. 1080) and then cooling it rapidly in water, brine, or oil. When steel is hardened properly, the grain is refined and made more uniform, but it is too hard and brittle for use.

3. *Tempering* is a process of reducing the degree of hardness by removing some of the internal strain, with the result that the steel is hard enough and tough enough to be useful but not brittle. This is done by heating the steel to a lower temperature, usually below 800°F, and then cooling it. A high-carbon or alloy steel article is always hardened and then tempered. Objects that have been forged may have to be annealed before they can be machined.

TABLE 47-1. COLOR AND TEMPERATURES

| Color | Metal temperature | |
	Degrees C	Degrees F
Faint red.............	482	900
Blood red............	566	1050
Dark cherry..........	579.5	1075
Medium cherry.......	677	1250
Cherry or full red......	746	1375
Bright red............	843	1550
Salmon..............	899	1650
Orange..............	940.5	1725
Lemon...............	996	1825
Light yellow..........	1079.5	1975
White................	1204	2200
Dazzling white........	1288	2350

You will be doing the older methods of heat-treating, which are sufficient for small shops. In industrial plants heat-treating has become a highly technical

153

and scientific occupation, and the individuals responsible for it must know a great deal about metallurgy and about the operation of scientific gauges and equipment. Each different kind of steel must be heat-treated in a particular way so that it will perform its special function as a machine part. Machinists' and heat-treating handbooks will give you specific information on how to heat-treat each kind and type of steel.

In heat-treating the metals must be brought to a certain temperature in large furnaces (Fig. 47-1). The correct temperature is indicated on gauges. After being heated, the metal is placed in a water, brine, or oil bath for hardening and is then re-heated to a lower temperature in an oil bath for proper tempering. The same types of furnaces are used when annealing steel.

To be entirely satisfactory, steel parts must have a certain degree of hardness. There are two common methods of testing for hardness: one called the *Brinell hardness test*, in which a steel ball is

forced into the metal part and the diameter of the indentation measured, and another called the *Rockwell hardness test*, which is more common, in which a diamond point is forced into the steel and the degree of hardness automatically registered on a gauge (Fig. 47-2).

Many steel parts and tools that do not require extensive grinding may be made from less expensive low-carbon steel, that cannot be hardened in its original condition. These articles are *casehardened*. Casehardening is a process of adding carbon to the outside shell of the steel, perhaps about $\frac{1}{32}$ inch, and then harden-

Fig. 47-2. Testing the hardness of a piece of steel. The gauge automatically indicates the degree of hardness.

Fig. 47-1. This worker is operating an industrial-type heat-treating furnace that is hardening gun barrels. Huge furnaces are made to handle all sizes of metal parts.

ing the shell. This produces a hard exterior with a soft, tough interior.

Discussion Topics

1. Why is it necessary to heat-treat certain tools? What does the heat-treating do to metal?

2. Define "annealing," "hardening," and "tempering."

3. Name and describe the two hardness tests.

4. What is casehardening?

5. What skills and knowledge are needed in the heat-treating occupations?

Unit 48. Heat-treating Steels

You can do a very satisfactory job of heat-treating a cold chisel, center punch, or hammer head with simple equipment available in the shop. Remember: an article cannot be hardened and tempered unless it is made of steel that has a high carbon content. For tools that must be ground, only tool or alloy steel should be used. However, tools such as hammer heads or C clamps can be made of low-carbon steel and casehardened.

EQUIPMENT FOR HEAT-TREATING

A *blow torch, welding torch, forge or soldering furnace* may provide the heat if there is no special heat-treating furnace (Fig. 48-1). With a regular heat-treating furnace, a gauge called a *pyrometer,* can be used to indicate the correct temperature (Fig. 48-2). To cool the metal after hardening or tempering, you will need a *quenching bath.* This may be a pail or container of water, tempering oil, or brine.

HARDENING

Place the article in a furnace and slowly heat it. The correct heat can be determined by using a pyrometer or by watching the colors develop as shown in the color chart Table 47-1. After the correct temperature is reached, allow the article to soak up the heat until it is of even temperature throughout.

Remove the article from the furnace with tongs and plunge it in the quenching bath. Small tools should be put in point first or straight down since they will warp badly if one side cools faster

FIG. 48-1. A smaller heat-treating unit suitable for a school shop. The left side is a melting furnace that can be used in a foundry for melting metal. The center is a heat-treating furnace. The right side is a small general-purpose furnace that can be used for forging.

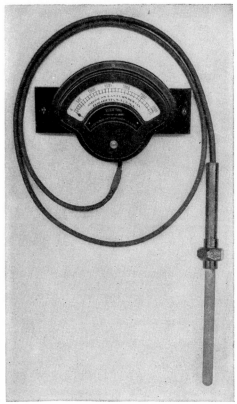

Fig. 48-2. A pyrometer. The end is inserted in the back of the furnace, and the correct temperature is then indicated on the gauge. This is the only accurate way of determining the correct temperature for hardening steels.

than the other. When hardening a thin article such as a knife, insert it by cutting the quenching bath with the hot metal. If the steel being used is oil-hardened, plunge it into the oil first until the color is gone and then into water.

TEMPERING

Determine the exact degree of hardness desired. See Table 48-1 for the exact temper color. If articles are to be tempered equally throughout, they are usually placed in a bath of tempering oil and the entire contents heated to the required temperature. However, most small tools require a hard point and a softer handle.

1. Clean the tool that has been hardened by removing the scale with abrasive cloth on one side at least.

2. Heat a block of steel in the furnace or forge to a red heat. Remove and place on a soldering or welding bench. Place the tool on the heated block with the point extending beyond. Now watch the temper colors run. When the exact color reaches the end of the tool, for example, straw color for center punches, plunge the tool in water again.

3. When tempering a knife blade, clean one side of the blade with abrasive cloth. Pack the cutting edge with wet asbestos. Apply heat to the back of the blade with a bunsen burner or welding torch until the proper temper color runs toward the edge. Plunge in water.

TABLE 48-1. TEMPER COLORS OF COMMON TOOLS

Tools	Color	Degrees F
Scriber, scrapers, and hammer faces......	Pale yellow	430–450
Center punches, drills.	Full yellow	470
Cold chisels, drifts....	Brown	490–510
Screw drivers.........	Purple	530

HARDENING AND TEMPERING

To harden and temper a small tool in one operation, first heat it to hardening temperature. Grasp the handle of the tool with tongs and plunge only the point of the tool in water, moving it back and forth to cool it. Then remove the tool, clean off the scale from one side of it with abrasive stick, and lay it on a welding or soldering bench. Watch the temper colors run from the hot handle toward the point. Replunge the entire tool in water.

ANNEALING

Heat the article to correct temperature, Table 47-1, and then do one of the following:

1. Place in a pail of sand.

2. Turn off the furnace and allow the piece to cool in it.

3. Clamp the article between two pieces of hot metal and allow it to cool in air.

CASEHARDENING

There are many methods of casehardening, but the only safe one for school, small shops, and home is to use some kind of carburizing material such as ground bone, leather, or a commercial product called *Kasenit*.

1. Pack the article in a box containing the carburizing material. Heat the entire box to temperature and allow it to remain in the furnace until the article is heated completely through to a bright red heat.

2. Remove the tool from the material and plunge it in water to harden the case.

Discussion Topics

1. Does the kind of metal determine the heat-treating method?
2. How is the metal heated?
3. Describe the method for hardening. For tempering.
4. Can a tool be hardened and tempered in one operation? Explain.
5. How do you anneal an article, and what effect does the annealing have on it?
6. Describe casehardening as done in the small shop.

Section VII. FOUNDRY

Unit 49. Introduction to Foundry

Whether or not you will ever make a casting, you will be interested in learning about foundry and its place in the metal-working industry (Fig. 49-1). Most metal articles used by the average family contain some cast parts. Everything from doorknobs, jewelry, and bathtubs to many parts of bicycles, automobiles, and other vehicles of transportation has parts made in the foundry (Figs. 49-2 and 49-3).

Since foundry work is primarily concerned with making molds and with melting and pouring metal, the operations are very different from any other metalwork. Castings are produced as described below.

A *pattern* of either wood or metal is made slightly larger but exactly like the finished casting. Most patterns are made of wood. The slightly larger size of the pattern allows for shrinkage of the metal as it cools and for any machining that may be necessary later. The pattern is used to make the *sand mold*. This is done by placing the pattern in a box,

Fig. 49-1. Here is a molder using production equipment to make a sand mold for an airplane-engine part. The pattern has been raised and you see the fine imprint in half of the sand mold.

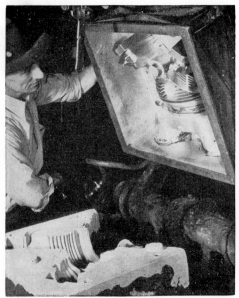

Fig. 49-2. Decorative castings, such as this dining table and chairs, illustrate the art of foundry.

called a *flask,* and packing sand around the pattern. Since the flask is made of two or more parts, it can be taken apart and the pattern removed. After the pattern is removed, a *gate* is cut to the *pour, or sprue, hole* and the mold is closed. However, if the finished casting must have holes or openings through it, these are provided by special *sand cores,* which are placed in the mold before closing. The molten metal is then poured into this cavity, and when it cools, the mold is broken up to remove the casting. Both the sand mold and the sand cores are used only once.

To finish the casting, the excess metal from the sprue hole and gate are cut off, the edges smoothed, and the casting cleaned. It may then be machined, welded, painted, or otherwise finished for use.

Some castings are made in metal molds, principally those from metals or alloys that melt at low temperatures, and these are called *permanent-mold castings, or die castings.* Small articles such as car-door handles are made in this manner.

All types of metals, including wrought iron, cast iron, steel, copper and, aluminum can be cast. The greatest number of castings, however, are made from gray cast iron.

A foundry requires all kinds of help—engineers, technicians, skilled labor, and unskilled workers. The man who controls the quality of the metal that goes into the casting and checks the performance of all cast parts is usually an *engineer* or a *foundry technician.* The patterns are made by a skilled wood- and metal-worker called a *patternmaker* (Fig. 49-4). The great majority of the skilled workers who actually make the molds are *molders,* and the specialized group of men who make the cores are called *coremakers.* The furnace operator is a *melter,* and the worker who pours the castings is called the *pourer* (Fig. 49-5). Men who finish and clean the castings are called *chippers* and *grinders.* Altogether, well over one-third of a million men work in foundries throughout the nation.

The smaller plants are called *jobbing*

Fig. 49-4. This huge wooden pattern will be used in making a casting for a large industrial machine. Since the pattern must be very exact, this patternmaker must be a highly skilled woodworker.

Fig. 49-3. A typical small pattern and casting for a part of a bench vise similar to those you use every day in the shop.

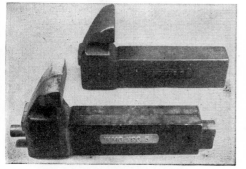

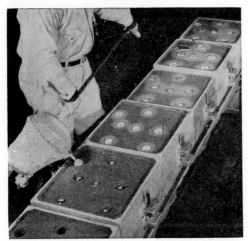

Fig. 49-5. Pouring molten metal into molds to form small castings. The metal is poured into one hole (sprue hole), fills up the cavity and sprue hole, and the excess metal rises up into the riser holes.

foundries since they make many different kinds of small castings and will often make one of a single article on order. Near large industrial centers there are *production foundries* in which hundreds or thousands of men make a few different castings. Over half of the foundry jobs

in the United States are done in Illinois, Ohio, Pennsylvania, and Michigan.

A new method of making castings is the compression of powdered cast iron into molds with large hydraulic presses. This eliminates the necessity of making a mold, melting the metal, and pouring it.

For people interested in modelmaking, pouring small castings can be a lot of fun and a fascinating hobby. Small parts or fittings for model airplanes, trains, and boats can be made in sand, plaster, or metal molds. Those interested in jewelry making can form molds of plaster of paris to make brooches, rings, and other small pieces.

Discussion Topics

1. Where are castings used?
2. What are the jobs and careers in foundry, and what does each entail?
3. Tell about the new method of making castings.
4. Can foundry work become a hobby activity?

Unit 50. Making a Cast Project

There are many small projects, such as ash trays, book ends, paperweights, the base for a buffing wheel, and parts for a model engine, than can be cast in a manner similar to that followed in a commercial foundry (Fig. 50-1). Such casting is a worth-while experience and one that will require great attention to detail (Fig. 50-2).

PATTERNMAKING

A pattern is needed to make the sand mold into which the metal is poured. This pattern may be made of wood, metal, or plastic, but most of them are made from a good grade of white pine. The original of the article can also be used as the pattern. The pattern must be somewhat larger than the finished size

FIG. 50-1. Small trays, book ends, trivets, letter openers, paperweights, and many other small articles may be cast in the shop.

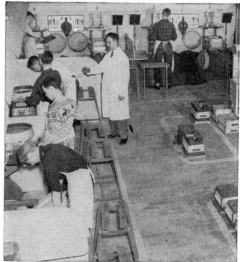

FIG. 50-2. The corner of a school foundry area. The boys are doing a variety of foundry operations. Notice the foundry tools and the completed sand molds on the floor.

because metal shrinks when it cools and because many castings require machining later. The extra size for shrinkage is provided by using a *shrink rule,* a scale on which the inches are longer than regulation inches. In the making of small decorative objects shrinkage does not have to be considered.

A pattern must also have *draft;* that is, it must be tapered so that it will lift out of the sand mold easily. If the pattern has no draft, the mold will break when the pattern is removed. Inside sharp corners on patterns are slightly rounded by the gluing in of leather or wood fillets.

Simple patterns are one piece. More complicated patterns, such as round objects or irregular shapes, are made in two or more parts, called a *split pattern* (Fig. 50-3). If the casting must have a hole or opening through it, the pattern is built

to provide for sand cores that form the openings. This sand core is made by mixing sand and a special binder and packing it in a small box called the *core box* (Fig. 50-4). This core may be used as is or can be baked so that is will be more solid.

To make a simple pattern similar to the one shown in Fig. 50-5 for a house sign, proceed as follows:

1. Cut the background for the pattern from a piece of plywood. Make sure that the edges taper slightly to form the draft. If you cut the piece out on a jig

FIG. 50-3. A split pattern. The completed mold of this pattern is shown in Fig. 50-19.

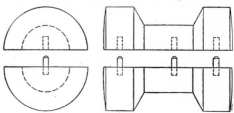

FIG. 50-4. A pattern and the casting for the other part of the vise shown in Fig. 49-3. The core box is in the foreground. A sand core is made by packing this box full of sand. This sand core fits into the mold to form the opening in the casting.

FIG. 50-5. A pattern for a house sign that you can make.

saw, tilt the table 2 to 3 degrees, and then do all the cutting from one side of the blade.

2. Cut out the letters that will form your name in the same manner, making provisions for proper draft.

3. Fasten the letters to the background with small brads.

4. Apply two coats of shellac colored black with lampblack to give it a commercial appearance.

MOLDING SAND

The sand for making the mold must be a special kind called *molding sand*. It must be heat-resistant, must stick together well and retain its shape, must be penetrated easily, and must have tempering qualities. This sand is found in several sections of the country, principally in the eastern Great Lakes states, in Kentucky, and in Missouri. When new, this sand is light-colored, but it becomes dark with use. The sand dries out when used or when it stands around and must be tempered by the addition of moisture. This is done by sprinkling water on the sand and mixing it in with a shovel. The sand is tempered properly when a clump picked up and squeezed will retain the sharp impression of your fingers. It will feel moist to your hand and will break off sharply when tapped.

A dry type of powdered sand called *parting sand* is dusted between the parts of the mold to keep them from sticking together. This is a fine lake or beach sand. Talcum powder can also be used.

FOUNDRY EQUIPMENT

A limited amount of equipment is needed for simple foundry work, including a flask, two molding boards, flask weight, bench rammer, sprue pin, riser pin, draw spike or screw, rapping bar, strike-off bar, riddle, molder's bulb, spoon and slick, gate cutter, slick and oval, bellows, sprinkling can, other molder's tools, and shovel (Fig. 50-6).

A furnace is also needed. For softer metal either a large soldering furnace or a special melting furnace can be used (Fig. 50-7). Some metals can also be melted in a forge or with a welding

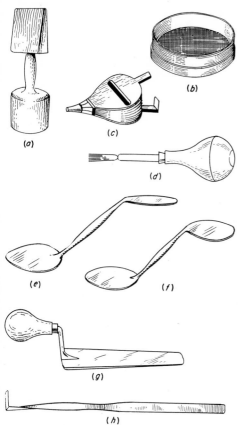

FIG. 50-7. A small melting furnace. Another type is shown in Fig. 48-1.

FIG. 50-6. Some foundry equipment: (a) bench rammer; (b) riddle; (c) bellows; (d) molder's bulb; (e) spoon and gate cutter; (f) slick and oval; (g) finishing trowel; (h) lifter.

torch. The metal is melted in a crucible or ladle. The pourer must wear canvas or asbestos gloves, leggings, and goggles for protection.

METALS

All types of metal can be melted and poured into castings, but many must be heated to a very high temperature with special equipment. See Table 50-1. There are many of the so-called softer nonferrous metals that can be easily heated with equipment available in the

TABLE 50-1. MELTING POINT OF METALS

Metal	Degrees F
Tin	449
Lead	621
Zinc	787
Zamak	736
Gar alloy	830
Aluminum	1217
Copper	1981
Iron	2786

average shop. Pure lead or an alloy of lead and antimony, called *type metal*, are good for simple projects. Aluminum or an alloy of zinc, copper, aluminum, and

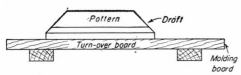

FIG. 50-8. The pattern is in correct position on the molding turn-over board. Notice that the pattern is placed with the draft upward.

magnesium, called *die-casting metal* or Zamak, is excellent. To help purify the metal during the melting process, a flux should be added. Powdered charcoal is needed for lead and special fluxes for aluminum, brass, or other alloys.

MAKING A SIMPLE MOLD

1. Select or make a pattern of the article or piece to be cast.

2. Place the pattern on the molding turn-over board with the tapered or draft side up (Fig. 50-8).

3. Place the drag of the flask face down on the molding turn-over board with the pins toward the board.

FIG. 50-9. Riddling sand into the drag. Pack it firmly around the pattern and into the corners with your fingers.

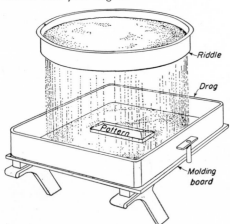

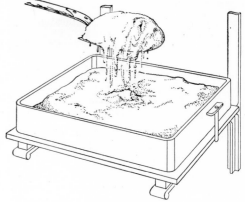

FIG. 50-10. Sand is added just as it is from the sand pile until the drag is overflowing.

4. Dust the pattern with parting sand or talcum powder.

5. Shovel some molding sand into the riddle, and shake it back and forth over the flask, covering the pattern thoroughly with sand (Fig. 50-9). With your fingers press the sand around the pattern and into the corners of the flask. The sand should cover the pattern to a depth of about $1\frac{1}{2}$ inches. When this is thoroughly packed, shovel in some more sand, just as it is, to a depth of about 2 inches more (Fig. 50-10).

6. Ram the mold, that is, use the rammer with the peen end first and then the butt end, packing the sand around the pattern and into the corners of the flask. This is very important, for in order to get a good casting you must have a good sharp impression of the pattern.

7. Continue to add sand, ramming it with the butt end until the flask is heaping full (Fig. 50-11).

8. Strike off the excess sand by using a metal or wood bar with a straight edge, working it back and forth, pulling the sand off the top of the flask (Fig. 50-12).

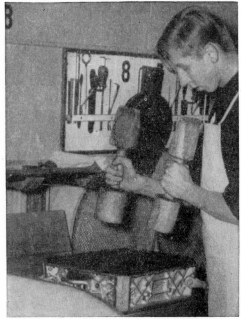

Fig. 50-11. Ram the drag, first with the peen and then with the butt end of the rammer until the sand is firmly packed.

Then place the bottom molding board over the drag (Fig. 50-13).

9. Hold the two molding boards tightly together and turn the drag over

Fig. 50-12. Strike off the drag, using a straight stick or a piece of metal. Work the stick back and forth as you push it across the drag to level it off.

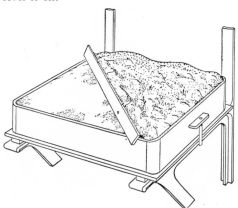

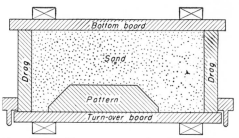

Fig. 50-13. Here you see the drag rammed with another molding board that is placed on top. The drag is now ready to be turned over.

(Fig. 50-14). Now lift off the turn-over molding board. You will see the bottom of your pattern and the even surface of the sand. Carefully blow off any extra particles of sand from the surface. Smooth any rough spots with a slick, trowel, or spoon and then dust the surface with parting sand or talcum. Blow off the excess sand with a bellows.

10. Place the other half of your flask, called the *cope,* in position. Make sure that it slips on and off easily.

11. Insert the sprue pin at a distance of about 1 to 2 inches from the pattern and about $\frac{1}{4}$ to $\frac{1}{2}$ inch into the sand, to

Fig. 50-14. Turning over the drag.

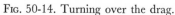

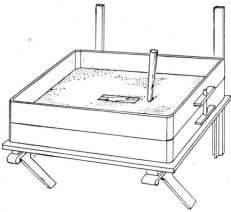

Fig. 50-15. Remove the turn-over board, place the cope in position, then the sprue pin and, if one is used, a riser pin. Dust the surface with parting sand.

hold it in position (Fig. 50-15). This will make the hole through which the molten metal will run. If desired, a riser pin may be inserted in position. This pin provides a hole into which the excess metal can rise up as the casting is poured.

12. Repeat the same thing you did in

Fig. 50-16. Ram the cope section as you did the drag. Notice, in using a split pattern, that the second half is put on after the drag is turned over. When this is completed, carefully remove the sprue pin and the riser pin.

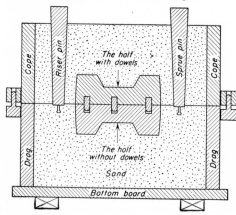

steps 5 to 8 for the upper half of the flask (Fig. 50-16).

13. To help the gases escape as the metal runs into the mold, it is necessary to vent the pattern by punching small holes in the cope half of the sand within $\frac{1}{2}$ inch of the pattern. This can be done with a darning needle or a piece of sharp, smooth wire.

14. Wiggle the sprue pin a little to all sides and then carefully pull it out. With your fingers pack the sand around the top of the sprue hole to make a funnel shape. Also remove the riser pin if one was put in.

15. Remove the cope or top half of the flask and set it on edge out of the way (Fig. 50-17).

16. With a molder's bulb or a little brush and a glass of water, carefully moisten the sand around the pattern. Do not get it too wet. This will help the mold to retain its shape as the pattern is removed.

17. Force a draw spike into the wood pattern and then lightly tap the spike on

Fig. 50-17. Remove the cope section and set it on edge.

all sides a little at a time to loosen the pattern from the sand. *Now carefully draw straight up on the pattern.* If this is done correctly, there should be a cleancut print in the sand (Fig. 50-18). If there is a little breaking off of the sand, you can repair it with any of the molder's tools. If a metal pattern is used, a threaded rod must be screwed into the pattern to remove it.

18. Bend a little piece of sheet metal into a U shape, and carefully cut a little groove or gate about 1 inch wide and $\frac{1}{2}$ inch deep from the pattern to the sprue-pin hole. Do not try to do this in one stroke. Cut a little distance and then throw the sand out of the way. This will form the gate through which the molten metal will run. Cut a gate to the riser hole if a riser pin was used. Press down any loose sand in the gate passage (Fig. 50-19).

19. Repair the mold as necessary by adding small bits of sand and smoothing them down with one of the molding tools of correct size and shape. Blow off any loose particles of sand with the bellows.

20. Close the mold by replacing the cope. Carefully guide the cope by placing your fingers along the side so that the pins of the drag line up with the holes of the cope (Fig. 50-19). The mold should now be placed on the floor and covered with a metal weight. If you are not going to pour the casting immediately, cover the sprue and riser holes so no dirt will fall into them.

POURING THE CASTING

1. *Dress safely.* To protect yourself, wear a pair of canvas or asbestos gloves, leggings, and a pair of clear goggles.

2. Select a ladle or crucible large enough for the mold to be poured. Place the pieces of metal or alloy in this container.

3. Heat until all the metal is at pouring temperature. Add flux and stir. All the impurities will come to the top and can be skimmed off.

4. Stand away from the mold, and pour the metal by holding the ladle away from you, making sure that you pour it evenly and quickly (Fig. 50-20). As soon as the metal comes in contact with the

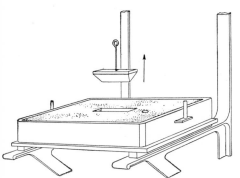

FIG. 50-18. Remove the pattern. Cut a gate to the sprue hole and to the riser hole, if one is used.

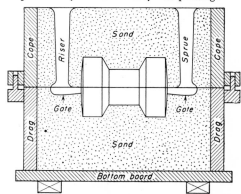

FIG. 50-19. Close the mold by replacing the cope. Here you see it ready for pouring.

Fig. 50-20. Pouring the metal into the molds. Notice that a heavy weight has been placed on the molds to keep the two parts together. Observe the protective clothing worn by the pourer.

sand, it will begin to solidify. Stop pouring as soon as the sprue hole is full. Keep your face and body away from the mold because steam will rise and the metal may spurt out. In some cases, if the mold is not vented properly, it can explode.

5. Allow the metal to cool and then break up the mold and remove the casting.

FINISH THE CASTING

1. Cut off the metal that forms the sprue and riser holes and the gates with a hack saw.

2. File or grind the edges smooth. On decorative castings, apply a scratchbrush finish. On other types of castings it will be necessary to machine on a drill press, lathe, shaper, or milling machine. Decorative castings are frequently painted, enameled, or lacquered, and a felt base added.

Discussion Topics

1. Define: "split pattern," "flask," "core," "gate," "sprue hole."
2. Tell how to make a simple pattern.
3. What are the characteristics of good molding sand?
4. Must any special clothing be worn? Explain.
5. What metals can be cast?
6. Give a short summary of the procedure for pouring a mold.
7. How are metals melted for pouring?
8. How are castings finished?

Section VIII. WELDING

Unit 51. Introduction to Welding

Welding is a process of joining two pieces of metal by heating the edges or surfaces until they become molten, thus fusing them together. The two most common types are *oxyacetylene* and *arc welding*. Oxyacetylene, or gas welding as it is sometimes called, utilizes burning gas—acetylene mixed with oxygen—to produce the heat; arc welding is done with a heavy electric current or amperage flow. Arc welding is faster and is used primarily in heavy production, while acetylene welding is best for light assembly and for many repair jobs. Arc welding, for example, has largely replaced riveting in most structural-steel work such as that in the framework of buildings, bridges, and ships (Fig. 51-1). There are many other types of welding such as spot, thermite, or oxygen-hydrogen, but all these operate on the principle of producing heat with either a gas flame or electric current.

Science has discovered another method of welding, however, that requires no heat. This process, called *cold weld*, is performed by merely applying enough pressure to fuse the two metals together.

In gas welding the operator holds a lighted torch into which the two gases are fed, acetylene with enough oxygen to make the hottest part of the flame burn at 6300°F (Fig. 51-2). The metal is heated until it becomes molten, and then welding rod is fed into the molten puddle to build up the weld. The torch is moved along slowly as the welding progresses.

In arc welding an electric generator or transformer steps up the amperage or flow of current. There are two exterior wires to complete the circuit. One of these is connected to a metal table on which the welding is to be done or to the object itself. The other is connected

Fig. 51-1. Arc-welding bridge reinforcements. In the background you see the generators that supply the electric current. Notice that welders wear special protective clothing to protect themselves from the sparks and dangerous rays.

Fig. 51-2. The torch this man is holding is supplied with acetylene and oxygen gas. The flame burns at a temperature of 6300°F. In his left hand he is holding a welding rod. To weld the joint, he melts the two adjoining edges and then adds welding rod to build up a bead.

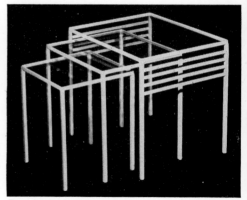

Fig. 51-3. This nest of tables is an example of the type of project that is assembled by welding. Made of tubing, angle iron, and glass, they are a most attractive project.

to a holder which holds the electrode, a rod of the same metal as the object being welded. To weld, the operator momentarily touches the end of the electrode to the article to complete an electric circuit and then pulls it away slightly to form an air gap. The heavy current overcomes the resistance of the air and forms an arc which produces a heat of about 9,000°F. This heat melts the metal and also the electrode; so the operator must feed the electrode into the joint as it is moved along. When the electrode is used up, a new one is slipped into the holder, and the welding is resumed.

In production, such as in automobile bodywork, a great deal of *spot welding* is done, in which a combination of heat and pressure fuses the metals. The two pieces are pressed tightly together between the points of an electric circuit and a heavy flow of current is passed through them, melting the metals at one spot and fusing the pieces together.

It is difficult to know just how many people earn a living at welding since hundreds of thousands who do welding are classified in some other occupation. There are thousands of jobs in manufacturing in which welding must be done. There are also thousands of other artisans, such as the auto mechanic, the blacksmith, the sheet-metal worker, the aviation mechanic, and the farmer, who do welding as part of their jobs. Welding is also used in making all types of artistic metal articles (Fig. 51-3).

Discussion Topics

1. What is "welding"?
2. Name the kinds of welding and describe each briefly.
3. In what occupations are welders employed?

Unit 52. Gas or Oxyacetylene Welding and Brazing

The beginner can master a few of the basic essentials of gas welding and do a reasonable job of joining low-carbon steels by welding or brazing cast iron, steel, copper, and other metals. Strict attention must be paid to the welding fundamentals and to rules of safety.

EQUIPMENT

Figures 52-1 and 52-2 show the major equipment necessary for gas welding. Note the names for each piece. The oxygen tank, which is the largest, is usually painted a dark green, and the acetylene tank, which is smaller, is usually painted black. The hose running from the acetylene tank is red or black, and that from the oxygen tank is green. The *welding torch* or *blowpipe* comes equipped with several different size *tips*. These tips are interchangeable, and, in general, a smaller tip is used on lighter materials and a larger tip for heavier materials. The smallest tip is usually used when welding $\frac{1}{16}$-inch stock.

The welder must always wear a pair of welding goggles.

The torch is lighted with a *spark lighter.* A welding table or bench with the top covered with firebrick should be ready to hold the work.

WELDING ROD

In most welding, additional metal must be added to build up the joint and form a bead. This welding rod should be the correct diameter and must be suited to the particular kind of welding. For example, for welding mild steel, choose a $\frac{1}{16}$-inch mild-steel welding rod for $\frac{1}{16}$-inch metal. Complete information regarding kind and size of welding rod is available from manufacturers.

ADJUSTING THE WELDING OUTFIT AND LIGHTING THE TORCH

It can be assumed that the beginner will start with a welding outfit that has already been assembled. If not, instructions are always supplied with a new welding outfit.

1. Put on a pair of goggles, leaving them over your forehead.

FIG. 52-1. An oxyacetylene welding outfit including everything but the tanks of gas: a torch with five tips, the hose, two regulators, goggles, friction lighter, and wrenches.

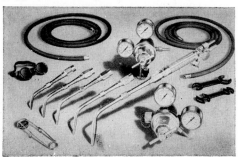

FIG. 52-2. The welding outfit hooked up and ready for use.

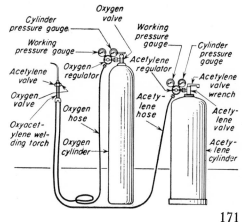

171

2. Select the correct size tip, and screw it into the torch. You will learn from experience how to make this selection; for welding ⅛-inch band iron, the second or third smallest tip is best.

3. Turn out the adjusting screws on the regulators as far as they will go to relieve all pressure.

4. Now turn the valve on the oxygen tank until it is as far open as it will go. Open the acetylene tank with a tank wrench. The cylinder pressure gauge of the regulators will show the amount of pressure of both acetylene and oxygen that remains in the tanks. If either of these reads zero, the tank is empty and must be replaced.

5. Turn in the adjusting screws on the regulators until the working pressure gauges show a pressure of about 5 to 10 pounds on both the acetylene and oxygen. Specific recommendations on gauge pressures can be found in the manufacturer's handbook for each particular kind of welding outfit.

6. Open the screw valve on the torch handle marked acetylene about a quarter turn, and light the torch with the scratch lighter (Fig. 52-3). Adjust the amount of acetylene gas until the flame just jumps away from the tip. Then turn on

the oxygen a little at a time until the desired flame is obtained. For most welding the neutral flame is best, that is, equal parts of oxygen and acetylene (Fig. 52-4). This flame has a full inner cone and does not have a feathery edge. If there is too little oxygen, the flame, which is called a *carburizing, or reducing, flame,* has an intermediate cone between the inner and outer cones. If there is too much oxygen, the outer cone is greatly shortened, and the torch gives off a hissing sound. A little practice will show you when a neutral flame has been secured.

7. When turning off a torch, close the acetylene valve first, then the oxygen.

8. When you have finished welding for the day, turn off the torch, turn out the screws on the pressure regulators, close the valves on the acetylene and oxygen tanks, and, finally, open the torch valves to release all pressure in the hoses.

Making Practice Welds

Before attempting to weld anything useful, you should make enough practice welds to do a proficient job on the finished article. Place goggles over your eyes. Begin your exercises as follows:

1. *Butt weld without rod.* Cut two pieces of scrap steel about $\frac{1}{16}$ by $\frac{3}{4}$ by 5

Fig. 52-3. Using the friction lighter to light the torch. *Never light it with a match.*

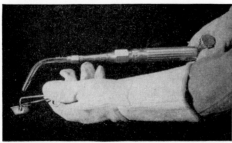

Fig. 52-4. A neutral flame is obtained by burning an equal mixture of oxygen and acetylene. The pale-blue core is called the *inner cone.* At the tip of this inner cone is the highest temperature. This is the proper flame for most welding.

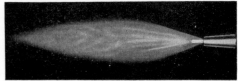

inches. Turn a $\frac{1}{16}$-inch flange on one edge of each piece. Place the pieces, with the flange edges together and facing up, about $\frac{1}{32}$ inch apart on the welding table. Hold the torch with the point of the inner flame just above the flange, about $\frac{1}{8}$ inch, at one end, and move the torch back and forth in a slight arc until the metal melts and tacks together. Then start at the other end to melt the flange to form a bead. Weave the torch back and forth slightly as you work from one end to the other. Keep the molten puddle of metal running to form a smooth, even bead.

Fig. 52-6. Two sheets properly spaced and tack-welded.

2. *Edge weld without rod.* Place two pieces of scrap metal together on edge. Tack one end, and then start at the other end to run a bead along the edge, joining the two pieces (Fig. 52-5).

3. *Butt weld with rod.* Cut two pieces of $\frac{1}{8}$-inch scrap stock and place them on the table about $\frac{1}{16}$ inch apart. On metal thicker than $\frac{1}{8}$ inch the edge must be ground to form a V. Tack the two ends together (Fig. 52-6). Select a piece of $\frac{1}{8}$-inch mild-steel welding rod. Form a puddle on one end, and then begin to

melt the rod into the puddle to build up the weld about 25 per cent. Weave the torch back and forth, moving the rod with just the opposite movement (Fig. 52-7). The bead is formed as shown in Fig. 52-8. If you get the tip of the flame too close to the weld, small blowholes will form, and the torch will pop or backfire. If you apply the heat primarily to the rod and not to the metals, the weld will fail to have proper penetration. The rod will

Fig. 52-5. Edge-welding without rod. This student is practicing to get a good bead and to develop good torch technique. It will take considerable practice to weld correctly.

Fig. 52-7. Welding a butt joint with a rod. Notice that the rod is placed just ahead of the flame.

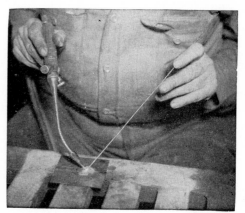

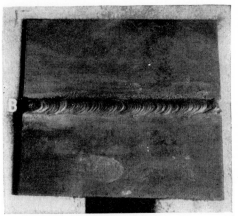

Fig. 52-8. The top surface of a good butt weld on sheet steel.

merely melt and drop on to the metal rather than fuse with it.

Other common joints or welds you should practice are the lap weld, fillet weld, tube to plate weld, tubular-butt weld, and vertical-butt weld (Figs. 52-9 to 52-14). After you have practiced sufficiently, you will be ready to weld some of your projects or to do repair jobs.

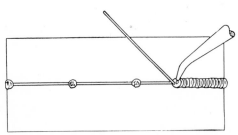

Fig. 52-9. Butt weld.

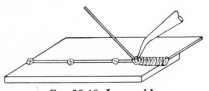

Fig. 52-10. Lap weld.

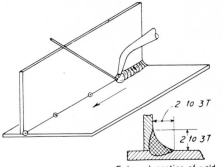

Fig. 52-11. Fillet weld.

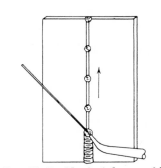

Fig. 52-12. Vertical butt weld.

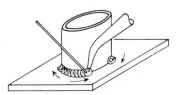

Fig. 52-13. Tube-to-plate weld.

Fig. 52-14. Tube butt weld.

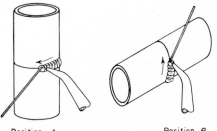

Position *A*   Position *B*

Brazing

Brazing is hard-soldering and is done in much the same way as silver soldering. It is employed frequently for repairing like or unlike metals or for making a joint that will be almost as strong as a welded joint without actual melting of the metal. A flux is needed as well as a brazing rod that is an alloy of copper, zinc, and several other metals. This flux can be borax, although a commercial flux is better.

1. Clean the two parts that are to be joined, by removing all oxide, paint, or other impurities. It is essential that both parts be perfectly clean. Place them on a welding table.

2. Heat the two metals to a red heat. If the parts are of unequal size, apply most of the heat to the heavier part.

3. When they have reached red heat, heat the end of the rod slightly, and stick it into the flux. Hold the end of the fluxed rod just ahead of the tip of the torch, and apply more heat to the metals until the flux and rod start to flow. Never melt the rod directly with the torch. It is easy to burn the brazed joint by over-heating, thus weakening it.

4. There are rods and fluxes available for doing low-temperature welding or brazing on aluminum, copper, stainless steel, Monel metal, and other alloys. Complete instructions on how to use these rods and fluxes are supplied by the manufacturer.

Discussion Topics

1. Name and describe the equipment needed for gas welding.
2. Why is it necessary to wear goggles?
3. How is gas welding done?
4. How does brazing differ from welding?

Unit 53. Arc Welding

If you have learned to do acetylene welding on various types of joints, you will not find it difficult to do elementary arc welding.

Equipment

Arc-welding equipment includes the *welder* (Fig. 53-1), which may be either a transformer or a direct-current generator with *two cables,* one connected to an *electrode holder* and the other to an all-metal welding table (Fig. 53-2). The second cable is called the *ground cable.*

In addition, you need a face shield (Fig. 53-3), heavy gloves, a chipping hammer, and a wire brush. The welding rod, which is clamped in the electrode holder, is called an *electrode* (Fig. 53-4). Since most arc welding is done on steels, this electrode is made of mild steel, either bare or covered with a flux which forms a shield when the arc welding is done (Figs. 53-5 and 53-6). Recommendations concerning the exact kind of electrode to choose for each kind of metal can be obtained from the manufacturer's literature.

Fig. 53-1. Motor-generator arc welder.

Fig. 53-3. Operators must always wear a head-shield helmet for arc welding.

Procedure

1. *Dress properly.* Place the face shield in the up position. Fasten the uncoated end of a $\frac{1}{16}$-inch coated electrode in the holder.

2. Adjust the welder to the proper amperage and voltage flow. For a $\frac{1}{16}$-inch electrode the amperage should be 30 to 60 and the voltage from 19 to 22. The larger the electrode, the higher the amperage and voltage should be.

3. Place a piece of scrap steel on the metal welding table. Drop the shield over your face and start the arc (Fig. 53-7). This can be done by either of two methods, as shown in Fig. 53-8. Touch the

end of the electrode momentarily to the metal, and then pull it back until the arc forms. If you pull it away too far, the arc will be broken. If you leave it on the

Fig. 53-4. The electrode holder holds the electrode.

Fig. 53-2. The welding circuit for arc welding. The ground cable, or lead, can be attached to the work or to a metal table.

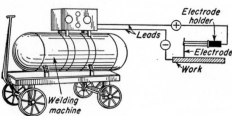

Fig. 53-5. Arc-welding with the bare electrode.

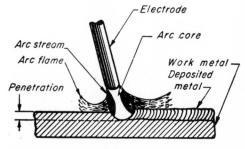

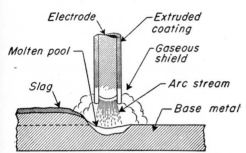

FIG. 53-6. Welding with the coated electrode.

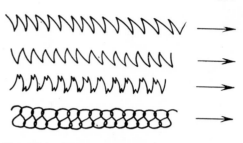

FIG. 53-9. These are some of the weaving motions that can be done in welding.

FIG. 53-7. The welder is about to start the arc. When he touches the end of the electrode to this motor, the circuit will be completed.

FIG. 53-8. Two methods of starting an arc.

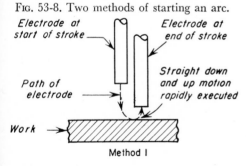

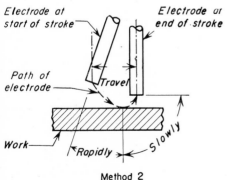

metal too long, the electrode will stick. Break it off quickly by twisting the rod.

5. Keep the electrode the same distance from the metal at all times, and move the holder forward in a weaving motion (Fig. 53-9) as you feed the electrode into the molten puddle.

6. When the electrode has been used up, clamp a new one in the holder. Clean the slag from the end of the weld, start the arc slightly ahead of the weld, bring it back to pick up the weld, and then continue forward (Fig. 53-10).

FIG. 53-10. Picking up the weld after inserting a new electrode in the holder. Notice that the arc is started slightly ahead of the completed weld(1), brought back of the crater (2), and then moved forward (3).

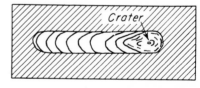

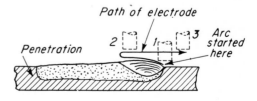

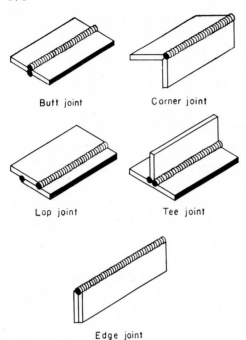

Butt joint   Corner joint

Lap joint   Tee joint

Edge joint

Fig. 53-11. Types of arc-welding joints.

It will require considerable practice to develop correct techniques of arc welding, but when these techniques have been mastered, all types of joints can be made (Fig. 53-11).

Discussion Topics

1. What is "arc welding"?
2. What equipment is needed?
3. Are any special safety precautions necessary?
4. Tell how to form an arc and how to use the electrode.

Section IX. MACHINE SHOP

Unit 54. Introduction to Machine Shop

In machine shop, metal is cut to shape on many different power-machine tools. There are five basic machine tools:

1. The *drill press* for drilling all sizes of holes and for boring, reaming, tapping, and other cutting operations (Fig. 54-1).

2. The *lathe* for turning metal to straight, tapered, or curved shapes, for cutting threads, and for drilling, boring,

FIG. 54-1. This radial-drill operator is drilling a heavy steel plate for a large piece of machinery. The arm of the machine can be swung to any position around the column and the drilling head moved automatically in and out along the arm to locate the spindle over the work.

and reaming (Fig. 55-1). A *turret lathe* and *screw machine* are types of lathes that do many operations in rapid succession (Fig. 54-2).

FIG. 54-2. A screw machine in operation. This is an adaptation of a lathe. Observe closely and you will notice that several different operations may be done in rapid succession. The machine is now ready to drill a hole, next it will cut inside threads, next turn outside diameter, and then cut outside threads.

Fig. 54-3. A shaper operator machining stock to thickness.

Fig. 54-4. A horizontal-milling-machine operator. This is a good production machine because it will remove a great deal of metal in a short time. Notice that the metal is held in a fixture so that each piece will be machined in exactly the same manner.

3. The *shaper* for finishing flat surfaces, cutting grooves, V's, and keyways (Fig. 54-3). It has a single-point tool on the end of a ram that moves back and forth to do the cutting. The *planer* operates on the same principle except that the work moves back and forth instead.

4. The *milling machine* for shaping metal, for cutting gears, and for many other operations. Its greatest value is that it removes metal faster than most other machine tools and that all shapes of cutters can be attached to do production work (Fig. 54-4). There are many different kinds, such as the horizontal, vertical, or universal, each for a different purpose.

5. The *grinder* for smoothing and shaping pieces that have already been machined and heat-treated. The abrasive wheel cuts the metal down to finished size. There are two types, the *surface grinder* for finishing flat work and the *cylindrical grinder* for cylindrical work (Figs. 54-5 and 54-6).

Pieces machined on these tools are usually cast in a foundry or made from standard bar, rod, or plate stock. These are shaped on the drill press, lathe, milling machine, shaper, or adaptations of these machines. They are then considered finished unless they are to be used in

Fig. 54-5. A surface grinder operator. The work to be ground is held tightly in position by a magnetic chuck. This large electromagnetic chuck is clamped to the top of the table. By shifting a lever, electricity magnetizes the chuck and holds the iron or steel object firmly in place. When the electricity is turned off, the chuck is demagnetized and the work may be easily removed. This operator should put on goggles before turning on the grinder.

Fig. 54-6. A cylindrical-grinder operator. Notice the mirror finish being obtained on this shaft by grinding. During the grinding a soluble oil helps to keep the work cool and improves the quality of the finish.

places where they will require great strength or be subject to excessive wear. In these cases, the pieces are machined to a few thousandths of an inch oversize, then heat-treated to proper hardness and toughness, and finished to size on grinders.

There are more people employed in machine-tool occupations than in any other phase of metalworking, a total of three-fourths to one million. The man who supervises and plans the work in the machine shop is usually an *engineer*. The *skilled machinist* can operate all the machine tools. The *tool- and die-makers* are the highest paid machinists. They make the cutting tools and special jigs and fixtures to hold metal parts that are to be machined. The diemaker makes metal dies or forms into which parts are stamped or into which metal or plastic is poured to make castings. The tool- and diemakers must work for several months before a new car, refrigerator, or other metal product can go into production. They make the new dies that stamp out the fenders, doors, and other parts and the new jigs that hold the parts to be machined. A man who operates only one machine is called a *machine operator*. A lathe operator, for example, spends all of his time running a lathe.

There is a machine shop in almost every community. The smaller ones are called *job shops,* and their work consists of general repair or the machining of small numbers of a single article. The large ones, called *production shops,* mass-produce articles. A complete line of small machine tools can be purchased for the hobbyist. Hobbies such as gunsmithing, modelmaking, metal spinning, and inventing are some that require machine tools.

Discussion Topics

1. Name the machines used in the machine shop and briefly describe the work of each.

2. There are many machine-shop occupations. Name them.

3. How can machine shop be turned into a leisure time activity?

Unit 55. The Lathe and Its Accessories

The engine lathe is one of the most commonly used machine tools and is usually the first one a beginner in machine shop learns to operate.

SIZE OF THE LATHE

The size is determined by the swing, or the largest diameter that can be turned in it, and the length of the bed. A common size for school and home workshops is a 9-inch swing with a 3-foot bed (Fig. 55-1).

PARTS OF THE LATHE

It is important to learn the names of the various parts of a lathe and what each is used for.

1. The *bed* is a heavy cast-iron frame, the top of which is finished in flat or V *ways.*

2. The *headstock assembly* is permanently fastened to the left end of the bed. It consists of the headstock spindle and the mechanism for driving it. The spindle itself is hollow with a taper on one end, this end being threaded on the outside. A soft center is slipped into the tapered hole, and a driving, or face, plate screwed on the spindle when turning work between centers. The headstock-spindle mechanism includes a step pulley and back gears, so that the lathe can be adjusted to at least eight different speeds. Power for the lathe is provided by an electric motor. With the belt in various positions on the step pulley of the headstock assembly, four different *speeds* can be secured. By using the back gears, four more speeds are obtained. Generally, in turning, the smaller the diameter, the faster the speed; the harder the metal, the slower the speed. The higher speeds are for filing and polishing; slower speeds are for knurling, thread cutting, drilling large holes, and reaming.

3. The *tailstock* can be moved along the bed and locked in any position. It is

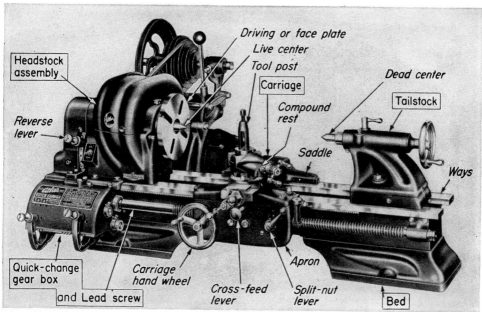

FIG. 55-1. The parts of a lathe. The live and dead centers are ground at an angle of 60 degrees. The cross-feed crank knob is just above the cross-feed lever.

made of two parts, so that the upper half can be moved to offset the tailstock for taper turning. The dead center, which is hardened, is fastened in the tailstock spindle for turning between centers.

4. The *carriage* consists of two parts: the *saddle* which is the I-shaped part resting on the top of the *ways*, and the *apron*, which is attached to the saddle and is the front part of the carriage. The saddle consists of the cross-slide mechanism and the compound rest and tool post. All the mechanism for operating the carriage movement and the cross slide is located in the apron. There is a hand wheel, to which is attached a pinion that meshes with a rack under the front of the bed. When the hand wheel is turned, the carriage is moved back and forth along the bed. There is also a *split-nut lever*, which is a power

feed for operating the carriage, and a power-feed lever for operating the cross feed automatically.

5. Directly under the front of the headstock assembly is a *quick-change gearbox*, which operates the *lead screw*. Three levers on this gearbox regulate the feed, or ratio, between the revolutions of the headstock spindle and the movement of the carriage. For example, if 8 threads per inch must be cut, the gears can be arranged, by means of the three levers, to make the headstock spindle revolve eight times for each inch the carriage moves. There is a lever just above the gearbox which will reverse the direction of the lead screw, and this will, of course, reverse the direction of the carriage or the cross slide. For ordinary turning the feed is set to equal about 36 threads per inch or a feed of 0.266 per revolution.

ACCESSORIES

1. *Chucks* are used to hold stock when facing the end, drilling, boring, reaming, and for other operations. When one is in operation, it replaces the driving plate. There are two types, the three-jaw universal and the four-jaw independent. The first is for beginners, because one turn of the key will move all three jaws simultaneously. This can be used only for

FIG. 55-2. Lathe accessories.

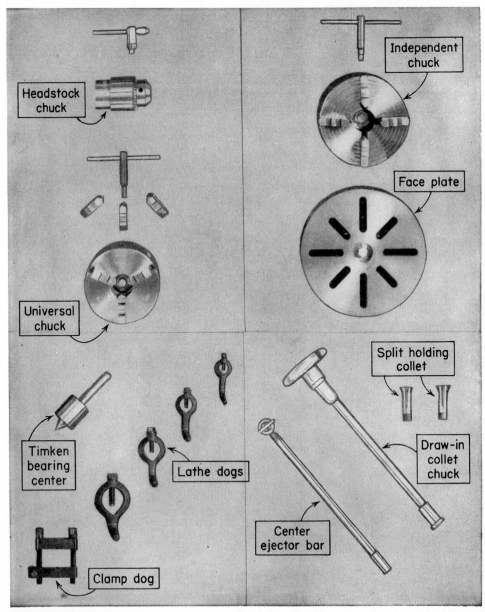

round work, however. The four-jaw chuck is arranged in such a way that each jaw must be adjusted individually, and this requires considerable skill (Fig. 55-2).

2. *Lathe dogs* are used for turning between centers. There are two types, the bent-tail and the clamped type, both of which are available in several sizes (Fig. 55-2).

FIG. 55-3. The proper method of grinding some of the common cutting tools. (*a*) A roundnose cutting tool; (*b*) a right-hand cutting tool; (*c*) a left-hand cutting tool.

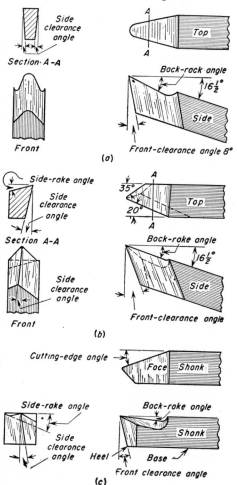

3. *Tool bits* are small rectangular pieces of alloy or high-speed steel. These bits must be ground to various shapes for different cutting operations (Fig. 55-3). While the shapes differ, each must have four clearance angles: a side and a front clearance to prevent the tool from scraping and a back and side rack to form the correct cutting edge.

To grind this tool, proceed as follows:

a. Dress the face of the abrasive wheel clean and true. Hold the side of the tool bit against the edge of the wheel to grind the side clearance, which should be about 10 to 12 degrees.

b. Swing the bit a quarter turn to grind the front clearance to about 8 degrees.

c. Grind the back and side rack at one time.

4. *Toolholders* hold the tool bit and are fastened in the tool post. There are three types: the left-hand, the straight,

FIG. 55-4. Parts of a micrometer: (*A*) frame; (*B*) anvil; (*C*) spindle; (*D*) sleeve; (*E*) thimble; (*F*) friction slip. This tool divides an inch into 1,000 equal parts. The horizontal line on the sleeve is divided into 40 equal parts, each representing 0.025 inch. Every fourth line is numbered 1, 2, 3, etc., indicating 0.100 inch, 0.200 inch, 0.300 inch, etc. The scale on the thimble is divided into 25 equal parts, each representing 0.001 inch.

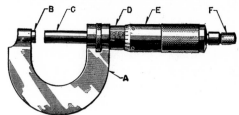

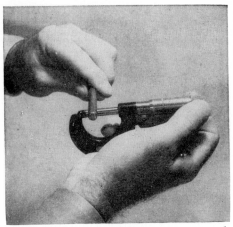

Fig. 55-5. Using a micrometer to measure the diameter of a rod.

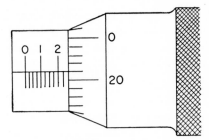

Fig. 55-7. A micrometer reading of 0.246 inch. Can you read this correctly?

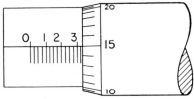

Fig. 55-6. Reading the micrometer. Notice that 13 full divisions on the sleeve scale are visible. Since each represents 0.025, this reading equals 0.325. In addition, the 15 divisions on the thimble scale mean that the spindle has advanced an additional 0.015 inch for a complete reading of 0.340 (0.325 + 0.015).

and the right-hand. A straight or right-hand type is most common (Fig. 56-6).

5. *Boring tools* and holders are needed for doing internal turning. The tool is ground to about the same shape as a bit for outside turning except that it must have a greater front clearance (Figs. 57-5 and 57-6).

6. *Measuring tools.* There are many kinds of precision measuring tools that the machinist must use. Four required by the beginner are a 6- or 12-inch ruler, inside and outside calipers, and a micrometer (Figs. 55-4 to 55-7).

Discussion Topics

1. Draw a sketch of the engine lathe, naming parts.
2. Tell how to adjust to different lathe speeds.
3. What are the different operations that can be performed on a lathe?
4. What are the lathe accessories used for?

Unit 56. Turning Between Centers

There are many operations performed with the stock held between centers, the most common of which are rough and finished turning, cutting a shoulder, facing an end, taper turning, knurling, filing, polishing and thread cutting. The first of these, rough turning, is basic to all of the other operations.

Select a piece of stock of the correct kind of metal, about ⅛ inch larger in

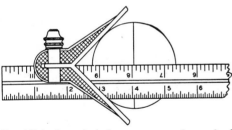

FIG. 56-1. Locating the center on the end of stock by using a center head.

FIG. 56-3. Using an automatic centering head to locate center.

diameter, and about 1 inch longer, than the finished size.

LOCATING AND DRILLING CENTERS

1. Locate the center on either end of the stock by one of the methods shown in Figs. 56-1, 56-2, and 56-3.

2. Select a combination drill and countersink of the correct size, usually a No. 2 for small-diameter stock.

3. Fasten this in a drill press and hold the work on end to drill the hole. The hole should be drilled until about three-fourths of the countersink has entered the metal. This can also be done on the lathe (Figs. 56-4 and 56-5).

ROUGH TURNING

1. Fasten a lathe dog to one end of the stock.

2. Move the tailstock assembly until it provides an opening between centers

FIG. 56-2. Using a hermaphrodite caliper to locate center.

slightly longer than the stock. Lock the tailstock in position.

3. Insert the tail of the lathe dog in the opening of the drive plate and place the work between the centers. Lubricate the dead-center end with a small amount of white or red lead and oil.

4. Turn up the handle of the tailstock

FIG. 56-4. Drilling the centers on the end of stock, using a combination drill and countersink on the drill press.

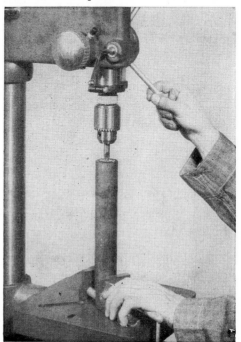

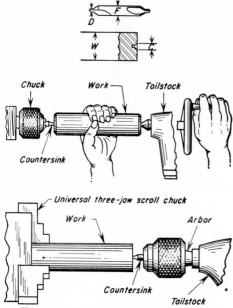

Fig. 56-5. Drilling centers on the lathe.

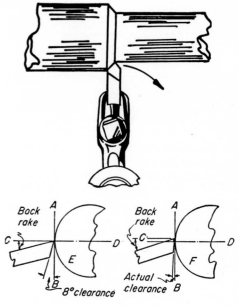

Fig. 56-6. Adjusting the cutter bit to correct position for rough turning.

until the work is held snug between centers, and then lock the spindle in position. It should not be so tight that the tailstock end heats up and burns or so loose that the lathe dog rattles.

5. Insert a tool bit in a toolholder and fasten it in the tool-post holder. Adjust the cutting edge of the tool to a point directly on center or slightly above and with the tool turned slightly away from the headstock (Fig. 56-6).

6. Adjust for the correct speed based on the kind of metal and the diameter of the stock. Adjust also for the feed: coarse feed for rough turning and fine feed for fine turning.

7. Move the carriage back and forth by hand. The point of the tool should clear the right end of the work. When turning, the point should go over half the length of the stock without the lathe dog striking the top of the carriage.

Check to see that the carriage will move in the right direction from tailstock to headstock when the automatic feed is on.

8. Set outside calipers to $\frac{1}{32}$ inch larger than the finished diameter (Fig. 56-7a).

9. Bring the point of the cutting tool to the extreme right end of the work. Turn on the power. With your right hand on the handle of the cross-feed and your left hand on the hand wheel, turn the cross slide in and the hand wheel toward the headstock until the cutting edge begins to remove a small chip. When the chip is started, throw in the lever for the automatic longitudinal feed (Fig. 56-8). Allow the cut to advance to slightly more than half the length of the stock. At the end of the cut simultaneously turn the cross-feed out and release the power-feed.

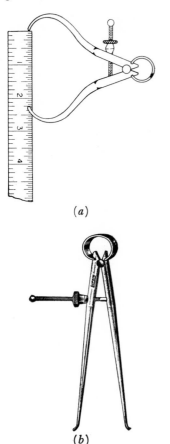

(a)

Fig. 56-9. Cutting a shoulder. A right-hand facing tool is needed to cut into a sharp corner. Adjust the tool so that the cutting edge is at right angles to the center line of the work.

(b)

Fig. 56-7. (a) Adjusting an outside caliper. Hold one leg over the end of the rule, and then turn the thumb nut out until the other leg indicates the correct measurement. (b) Inside caliper.

Fig. 56-8. Turning between centers. Notice the way the work is held and how the cutter bit is set.

10. Return the carriage to the starting position. Turn off the power and check the diameter with caliper. In this way you can determine the amount of material that is yet to be removed. Repeat the cutting operation until the first half is turned to rough size. If alloys, steels, or high-carbon steel are being turned, apply a little cutting oil. Remember to lubricate the dead center periodically. Rough-turn the second half.

FINISH TURNING

Re-sharpen the cutting edge of the tool bit and adjust the lathe to a higher speed and finer feed. Finish-turn the first half by the same general method as that used for rough turning. Place a piece of soft copper or brass under the lathe dog when finish-turning the second half to prevent marring the smooth surface.

CUTTING A SHOULDER AND
FACING THE ENDS

When a piece of several different diameters is needed:

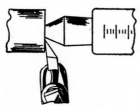

Fig. 56-10. Facing the end of stock. Bring the cutting edge up to the work and then turn the cross-feed crank out, taking a light cut.

1. Mark off the various lengths for the different diameters.

2. Rough- and finish-turn to size, leaving rounded corners.

3. Select a right- or left-hand cutting tool and adjust it with the cutting edges at right angles to the work (Fig. 56-9).

4. Cut out the sharp corner.

This same tool is used when facing the end of stock being turned between centers. It is desirable to place a half center in the tailstock end (Fig. 56-10).

Filing and Polishing

Adjust the lathe to a high speed. Hold a fine mill file as shown in Fig. 56-11. Take

Fig. 56-11. Filing. Use a mill file and take long, even strokes. The left-hand method is being used here because it is safer.

Fig. 56-12. Polishing with abrasive cloth. Apply a little cutting oil to the work and use a high speed.

long, even strokes across the revolving metal. Keep the file clean. Be careful not to hurt your arm on the revolving lathe dog. To obtain an extremely smooth polish, adjust the lathe to a high speed and smooth the surface with fine abrasive cloth. Apply a little oil to the cloth, and hold it around the revolving stock, moving it slowly from one end to the other (Fig. 56-12).

Knurling

The handles of many small tools such as punches, hammers, screw drivers, and clamps are knurled for better grip.

1. Adjust the lathe to the slowest possible speed and a very coarse feed.

2. Mark the length of the knurl on the metal.

3. Fasten the knurling tool in the tool-post holder at exact right angles to the work.

FIG. 56-13. Knurling. Make sure that the knurling tool is exactly at right angles to the work.

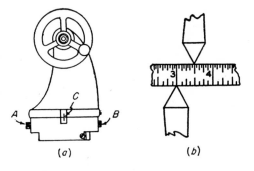

(*a*) (*b*)

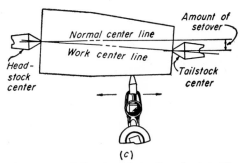

(*c*)

FIG. 56-14. Offsetting the tailstock. (*a*) The letters "A" and "B" indicate the setscrews and the letter "C" indicates the witness marks. (*b*) Using a rule to check the amount of offset. (*c*) Turning a taper with the work held between centers.

4. Begin at the extreme right end of the area to be knurled. Turn the knurling tool into the metal with a moderate amount of pressure. With the power off revolve the work once or twice by hand to see if the knurling tool cuts a sharp diamond shape. If not, it should be readjusted before turning on the power.

5. Turn on the power and apply a little oil to the knurling tool and to the work. Watch it carefully. Turn off the power as soon as the end of the knurl is reached.

6. If a deeper knurl is desired, turn in the cross-feed a little more, reverse the direction of the lead screw, and run the knurling tool back to the starting position. Never release the pressure on the knurling tool until the knurl is complete (Fig. 56-13).

TAPER TURNING

There are two common ways of cutting a taper:

1. Offsetting the tailstock

a. Figure the amount of taper.

$$\text{Offset} = \frac{TL}{L \text{ to be tapered}} \times \frac{LD - SD}{2}$$

(Total length over length to be tapered times large diameter minus small diameter over two.) The total length should always be the actual length of stock being turned, not the finished article.

b. Loosen the nut that holds the tailstock to the bed. Offset the tailstock by loosening or tightening the set screws found on both sides of the upper

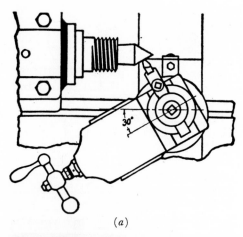

(a)

(b)

Fig. 56-15. (a) Cutting a short taper by setting the compound at the proper angle (one-half the included angle), and (b) feeding by hand by turning the compound-rest crank knob.

casting of the tailstock. Usually the tailstock is moved toward the operator so that the smallest end of the taper will be toward the tailstock. Measure the amount of the offset by holding a rule between the two witness marks or between the centers as shown in Fig. 56-14.

c. Install the work between centers and lock in position. Use a thin, round-nosed tool bit. Start the cutting about $\frac{1}{2}$ inch from the end of the stock, and continue to take a light cut until the small end is the correct diameter.

2. Using the compound rest

For short tapers the compound rest can be adjusted to the correct angle of the taper and the cutting done by using the compound (Fig. 56-15).

Discussion Topics

1. Name the operations that can be performed with the work held between centers.
2. Give a description of rough and finish turning.
3. How do you file and polish on the lathe? Cut a knurl? Turn a taper?

Unit 57. Chuck Work

Many operations such as drilling, boring, and reaming are performed with the work held in a chuck. For round stock a three-jaw universal chuck is used and for square or irregular-shaped work a four-jaw independent. Frequently, when a very accurate hole is needed it is first drilled $\frac{1}{16}$ inch undersize, then bored to $\frac{1}{32}$ inch undersize, and, finally, reamed to exact size.

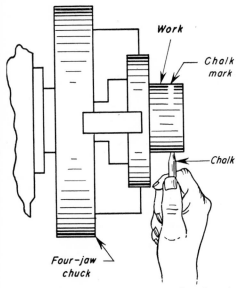

FIG. 57-1. Adjusting stock in a four-jaw independent chuck. The chalk will indicate where the work must be moved slightly away in order to center it.

FIG. 57-2. Facing the end of stock held in a three-jaw chuck. The carriage is locked to the bed by tightening the carriage-lock screw.

FASTENING STOCK IN A CHUCK

1. Remove the live center with a drive-out or ejector bar and unscrew the faceplate. If it sticks, put the lathe in back gear and strike the plate with a rubber mallet to force it off.

2. Clean off the threads. Place a wood board on the lathe bed, just under the headstock spindle. Lift the chuck on to the board.

3. Grasp the chuck in the center with your fingers and screw it on the spindle. Remove the wood board.

4. Open the jaws and insert the stock. Tighten the chuck with the chuck key. If an independent jaw chuck is used, each jaw must be tightened a little at a time to center the stock exactly. This can be checked as shown in Fig. 57-1.

FACING THE END OF STOCK

1. Insert a tool bit (Fig. 57-2).

2. Start the cut at the center of the stock and then use the automatic cross feed to face out from the center (Fig. 57-3). It is a good idea to lock the carriage when facing the end of stock by tightening the carriage lock nut. Of course, small diameters can be faced by operating the cross-feed by hand.

DRILLING

1. Remove the dead center and insert a drill chuck in the tailstock (Fig. 55-2).

2. Spot-center the hole, using a combination drill and countersink.

3. Select the size of drill desired. If it is a large one, a pilot hole will be needed.

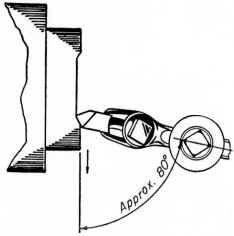

FIG. 57-3. Proper method of facing stock held in the chuck.

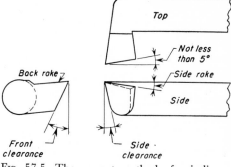

FIG. 57-5. The correct method of grinding a boring tool.

Insert the drill in the drill chuck or directly in the tailstock spindle if it has a tapered shank (Fig. 57-4).

4. Adjust the lathe for correct speed: fast speed for small drills and slow speed for large drills.

5. Drill the pilot hole if necessary.

6. Drill the finish hole. Lubricate the point of the drill frequently to prevent burning. Be careful not to drill into the headstock spindle.

BORING

Boring is done to cut a hole that is not standard size, to trim out a hole in a cast-

FIG. 57-4. Lathe drilling. The drill is held in a drill chuck if it has a straight shank. (See also Figs. 55-2 and 56-5.)

ing, or to cut a very accurate hole of any size.

The boring tool must be ground as shown in Fig. 57-5. This tool may be a forged tool or a cutter bit that is held in a boring bar (Fig. 57-6). Boring is done in the same general manner as external turning.

REAMING

Reaming is done to obtain a very smooth and accurate hole.

FIG. 57-6. Lathe boring. A boring bar is being used. The work is offset in a four-jaw chuck.

FIG. 57-7. Lathe reaming. Maintain a very slow speed and feed.

1. Adjust the lathe to a very slow speed.

2. Make sure that the hole is drilled or bored to more than $\frac{1}{64}$ inch undersize.

FIG. 57-8. Installing work on a mandrel using an arbor press.

FIG. 57-9. A gear blank is held on a mandrel and is being turned to finished size. Make sure that the tool-post wrench is removed before turning on the power.

3. Install the reamer in the tailstock spindle and feed it slowly into the work, using lard oil to lubricate it (Fig. 57-7).

TURNING STOCK ON A MANDREL

After a hole is drilled, bored, or reamed, the outside must frequently be turned down to size, as in making a gear blank or candlestick holder. To do this, you must fasten the work to a mandrel, which is a hardened piece of steel that has been tapered slightly.

1. Fasten the mandrel to the work in an arbor press (Fig. 57-8).

2. Turn the work between centers (Fig. 57-9).

Discussion Topics

1. What work can be done with the work held in a chuck?
2. How is work fastened in a chuck?

Unit 58. Operating the Shaper

The shaper was designed primarily to finish flat surfaces, although it can be used for many other operations, such as cutting V's, grooves, curved surfaces, keyways, and key seats. The size is indicated by the largest cube it will machine, a typical size for small shops being a 7-inch shaper. The major parts are shown in Fig. 58-1. All operating mechanisms are located on the right side and on top of the machine (Fig. 58-2). Some of the common adjustments are:

1. *Adjusting the height of the table.* This is necessary only under unusual conditions, when an extremely large piece of metal must be machined. To raise or lower the table, loosen the cap screws on both sides of the back of the crossrail. Place the hand crank on the lowest shaft and turn it to raise or lower the table.

After the adjustment has been made, tighten the cap screws and also adjust the front support for the table.

2. *Adjusting for length of stroke.* Turn the shaper over by hand until the ram is as far back as it will go. The pointer on the ram will then show the length of stroke. To lengthen or shorten it, hold the knurled nut (Fig. 58-2) in your left hand and place the adjusting crank on the square end of the shaft. Loosen the nut slightly, and then turn the crank until the pointer indicates the desired length of stroke. Tighten the nut again. The length of stroke should always be about $\frac{3}{4}$ inch longer than the stock to be machined.

3. *Adjusting for position of stroke.* Turn the shaper over by hand until the ram is as far forward as it will go. The

Fig. 58-1. Parts of a shaper.

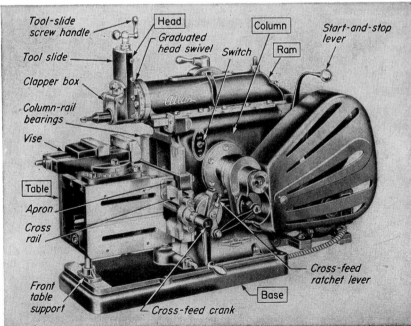

196

work should be clamped in position and the cutting tool in place. Loosen the hand clamp on the top of the ram (Fig. 58-2), and then, with the crank on the square end of the shaft at the back of the ram, make the adjustment until the point of the tool is about $\frac{1}{8}$ inch in front of the work. Tighten the clamp.

4. *Adjusting for speed.* On small shapers there are step pulleys for adjusting the belt in any one of four positions to change from slow to faster speeds.

5. *Adjusting for feed.* With the hand crank loosen the upper end of the link that operates the power feed (Fig. 58-2). Then offset this end of the link from the center. The farther off center it is, the greater the feed will be. Re-tighten after making the adjustment.

ACCESSORIES

The *shaper vise* holds most kinds of work. It is fastened to the top of the table and can be turned so that the jaws are either at right angles or parallel to the movement of the ram or at any angle in a 360 degree circle.

Parallels are rectangular pieces of steel made in pairs. They are used to block up the work in the vise. *Wedges,* or *holddowns,* are hardened pieces of steel that taper almost to a point. They are placed in the vise, as shown in Fig. 58-3, to hold the work firmly against the parallels.

The *toolholder* should be of a special type (Fig. 58-3). Do not use a lathe toolholder.

The *tool bits* for shaper work are very similar to those for lathe work except

Fig. 58-2. The control levers of a shaper for making common adjustments. Refer to circle numbers as you check for each adjustment.

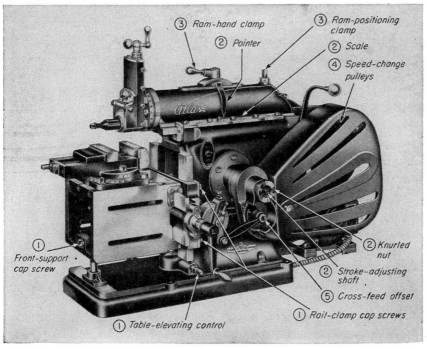

③ Ram-hand clamp
② Pointer
③ Ram-positioning clamp
② Scale
④ Speed-change pulleys
① Front-support cap screw
② Knurled nut
② Stroke-adjusting shaft
⑤ Cross-feed offset
① Rail-clamp cap screws
① Table-elevating control

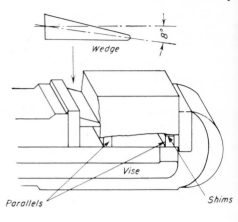

Fig. 58-3. Shaper accessories including shaper vise, parallels, hold-downs or wedges, bits, toolholder, and extension tool.

that they do not require so much side clearance. They do require a little more front clearance, however. A round-nose tool bit is suitable for most flat machining.

MACHINING A FLAT SURFACE

1. Fasten the stock in a vise using parallels and hold-downs. Insert the tool bit in the toolholder and fasten in the tool post. Check to see that the shaper head is at the zero position and that the clapper box is not offset.

2. Adjust for the correct length and position of stroke as well as for speed and feed. The cutting speeds should be determined by the length of stroke and the kind of metal being machined. The longer the stroke, the slower the speed; the softer the metal, the faster the speed.

The feed should be greater for rough cuts and less for finish cuts.

3. Place the hand crank on the end of the shaft that operates the cross-feed, and move the work until one edge of it is directly under the point of the tool.

4. Turn on the power. Place your right hand on the handle of the tool-slide screw and your left hand on the crank of the cross-feed. Turn the tool-slide down and move the cross slide until the point of the tool takes a cut of about $\frac{1}{32}$ to $\frac{1}{16}$ inch. Then trip the ratchet lever that engages the automatic cross-feed. You will be able to tell immediately if proper cutting action is taking place (Fig. 58-4). If the tool tends to chatter, the work or the tool is improperly clamped, the tool is ground incorrectly, the speed is wrong, or some

FIG. 58-4. Machining a flat surface. Notice the kind of toolholder being used.

FIG. 58-6. Cutting a taper. The tool head has been set at the correct angle, the clapper box offset. The cut must be made by using the hand vertical feed.

thing is loose. After one cut has been taken across the work; adjust the depth again. Reverse the ratchet that operates the cross slide, and take a second cut.

5. Continue to take cuts until the work is about 10 to 15 thousandths oversize. Re-grind the tool bit, adjust for a finer feed, and cut to the finished size.

FIG. 58-5. Machining a vertical surface. The clapper box, as you can see, is offset. This provides proper clearance for the tool on the return stroke.

FIG. 58-7. Cutting a keyway. An extension tool is needed to make an internal cut.

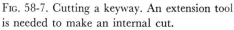

Making Vertical Cuts

1. Lock the work in the shaper with the end extending beyond the edge of the vise. Loosen the clapper box, and turn it so that the upper part of it slants away from the cutting direction.

2. Insert a right- or left-side cutting tool in the toolholder.

3. Check the toolslide by moving it down to the bottom of the work and then turning the shaper over by hand to make sure that the toolslide will not strike the column on the return stroke (Fig. 58-5). Return the toolslide to the upper position and then move the cross-feed over by hand until the point of the tool takes a slight cut from the end of the work.

4. Feed the tool down by hand to make the vertical cut.

Squaring Up a Block

1. Machine the largest flat surface.
2. Place this surface against the solid

Fig. 58-8. Machining a square on the end of a rod.

Fig. 58-9. Machining a rack.

jaw of the vise and machine the first edge.

3. Machine the first end of the stock by making a vertical cut.

4. Lay out the thickness, width, and

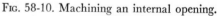

Fig. 58-10. Machining an internal opening.

length of stock on the block and repeat steps 1, 2, and 3.

Some other common operations that can be performed on the shaper are shown in Figs. 58-6, 58-7, 58-8, 58-9, and 58-10.

1. What is a "shaper"? How does it work?
2. How do you adjust for height of table? For length of stroke? For position of stroke? For speed and feed?
3. How is a flat surface machined?

Section X. METALS IN EVERYDAY LIVING

Unit 59. The Story of Iron and Steel

The principal users of steel in their order of consumption are automobile, truck and motor-vehicle manufacturers, construction companies, railroads, and tin-can producers. These four use over 40 per cent of the steel produced.

The following is a short description of how steel is made*:

Steel is largely iron; so the first step in its production is the smelting of ore in

* Joseph T. Ryerson and Son, Inc.

blast furnaces to obtain iron for later conversion into steel. Practically all of this iron ore comes from the Lake Superior region, which yields three types, each varying in iron content, chemical properties, and general appearance (Fig. 59-1).

Iron ore is but one of the four raw materials required in the production of iron. The other three are fuel, generally coke, a fluxing agent, which is usually limestone, and last but not least, air. It

Fig. 59-1. A view of one of the large open-pit iron mines of northern Minnesota. The tremendous size can be realized by looking at the men and cars in the foreground.

takes approximately 2 tons of iron ore, 1 ton of coke, ½ ton of limestone, and 4 tons of air to produce 1 ton of pig iron.

The blast furnace, which produces this pig iron, is a large steel shell, nearly 100 feet high, lined with heat-resistant brick (Fig. 59-2). It is charged through the top, with alternate layers of coke, ore, and limestone (Fig. 59-3). Each blast furnace has three or more stoves to heat air for the hot blast. Air is forced through the highly heated flues of these stoves and delivered to the blast furnace at temperatures ranging from 1200° to 1600°F. This air enters the furnace near the base and, in combination with the burning coke, produces a temperature of about 3500°F at that point.

When the oxygen in the hot air comes in contact with the highly heated coke, large quantities of carbon dioxide gas are produced, which, in turn, breaks down into carbon monoxide. Carbon monoxide is an active reducing agent; that is, it has the power of combining with oxygen and taking it away from other compounds such as iron ore. The carbon of the coke also reacts with the oxygen of the ore, and eventually, by means of these reactions, the iron is separated as a spongy, porous mass. As this porous iron moves downward into the higher temperature zone, it begins to melt and finally becomes entirely molten before it reaches the bottom of the furnace, or hearth.

The limestone which has been added with the other raw materials has the power of combining at high temperatures with the earthy impurities of the

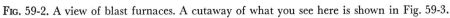

Fig. 59-2. A view of blast furnaces. A cutaway of what you see here is shown in Fig. 59-3.

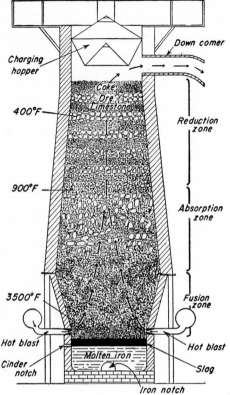

Fig. 59-3. Cross section of a typical blast furnace. Alternate layers of coke, ore, and limestone are charged in through the top of the furnace. As it passes downward through the furnace, the iron is separated and melted. The limestone and earthy impurities from the ore form a slag which, being lighter than the iron, floats on top. This slag is drawn off through the cinder notch leaving the clean iron to be drawn off through the lower iron notch.

picked up, largely from the coke, $3\frac{1}{2}$ to 4 per cent carbon.

A blast furnace operates continuously, the raw materials being supplied at the top as rapidly as necessary to provide sufficient hot metal for tapping at set intervals, usually 4 to 6 hours apart. One hundred to one hundred and twenty-five tons of liquid iron is taken from the furnace at each tap or cast. The liquid iron flows through troughs into huge ladles mounted on cars. This product of the blast furnace is usually referred to as *hot metal*. When cast into molds, it is termed *pig iron*. Steel is produced from either hot metal or pig iron by one of three methods—Bessemer process, refining in an open hearth, or refining in an electric furnace.

THE BESSEMER PROCESS

Hot metal from the blast furnace is poured into a Bessemer converter while it is tipped on its side. When it is turned upright, air pressure is forced through holes in the bottom of the converter (Fig. 59-4). The oxygen of the air blown into the molten iron burns out most of the silicon, manganese, and carbon. To this purified iron are added carefully proportioned amounts of carbon, manganese, or other elements, the amounts depending upon the kind of steel desired.

THE OPEN-HEARTH PROCESS

The open-hearth process is the one most generally used for making steel. In this process heat is directed over the metal instead of through it. The hearth resembles a large rectangular basin holding 50 to 175 tons of metal. In operation a

ore and forms a slag, which, being lighter than the molten iron, floats on top. This slag is drawn off through the *cinder notch* leaving the clean iron to be drawn off through a lower *"iron notch"* (Fig. 59-3).

During these operations the iron has

FIG. 59-4. One method of making steel. You see here the blow of one of the Bessemer converters. The air blast burns off the impurities and a great deal of the carbon, leaving the Bessemer steel.

charge of limestone and scrap is placed in the furnace (Fig. 59-5). The fuel, usually hot gas and air under pressure, enters at one end near the top of the furnace, ignites, and is directed downward and over the metal. After the scrap metal is nearly melted down—this usually takes about 2 hours—hot metal from the blast furnace is added, and the refinement of the metal continues. Most of the silicon and the greater part of the manganese are oxidized and combine with the limestone and other nonmetallic elements to form a slag, which floats on top, protecting the metal from the direct action of the flame. The carbon is gradually burned out, the amount allowed to remain in the steel depending on specifica-

tion requirements. Additional hot metal, manganese, or other alloying elements are added to produce steel of any desired analysis.

FIG. 59-5. A cross section of the open-hearth furnace, showing how the heat is directed on the metal instead of through it. The quality of steel can be carefully regulated.

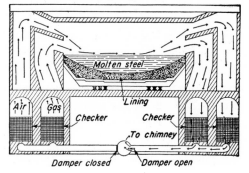

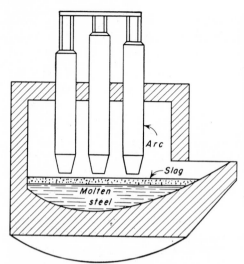

FIG. 59-6. A cross section of an electric furnace.

FIG. 59-7. A giant steel ingot about to enter the rolls of a blooming mill. This reduces the steel to a size that can be sent to the rolling mills.

THE ELECTRIC-FURNACE PROCESS

Steel is produced in the electric furnace in the same manner as in the open hearth except that it is usually in smaller quantities and that electricity is used for heating. The same types of steel can be produced by both processes (Fig. 59-6).

THE FINISHED PRODUCT

Steels produced by these methods are cast into ingot molds. The succeeding steps in manufacture vary, depending upon the product that is desired. For instance, in the production of sheets by the continuous-mill process, the steel in the ingot mold is allowed to cool enough to stand alone. The molds are then stripped off and the ingots sent to the soaking pits. Here they are held until they are heated throughout to a temperature of approximately 2200°F. A blooming mill then rolls the steel into a long strip about 4 inches thick and 3 feet wide (Fig. 59-7). The ends are cropped off, and the rest

cut into sections about 7 feet long. These slabs are sent to the reheating furnaces next to the continuous mill. When heated to the proper temperature, the slabs slide down an incline to the roll tables, which carry them through the roll stands. When a slab passes through these stands, it emerges stretched to a thin strip of steel 500 to 600 feet long (Fig. 59-8). These strips are rolled into coils ready for subse-

FIG. 59-8. The rolling mills. Notice how the sheets go through a series of large rolls, producing sheets of varying thickness.

quent finishing operations, such as annealing, pickling, cold rolling, etc.

Bars, structurals, and other steel products follow the same general method. The blooming mill reduces the ingot to the proper size bloom, slab, or billet. Special rolls continue the process reduction down to the finished form.

Sheets that are to be used for roofing, buckets, and other products that are likely to rust go through a process which first cleans them in an acid bath and then coats them with a thin film of pure zinc to make galvanized sheet, or they are coated with an alloy of tin and lead and called *terne plate*.

Sheets that are to be used for containers, kitchen utensils, pans, etc., are covered with a thin coat of pure tin and are called *tin plate*. To produce articles in which steel must resist corrosion, without putting on some surface coating of metal, an alloy called *stainless steel* has been produced. The principal kind contains 18 per cent chromium and 8 per cent nickel and is used wherever there is need for steel of great strength that will not rust.

Discussion Topics

1. Describe the process of making steel.
2. What are the three methods for making steel?
3. How are the many different shapes made, for example, sheets and bars?
4. In what ways is steel treated to make it more useful?

Unit 60. The Story of Copper

Copper, one of man's oldest and most versatile metals, has been used since the beginning of history for utensils, tools, and weapons. Copper's many desirable characteristics make it an all-important metal in the electrical world today. Since it conducts electricity easily, more of it is used for this purpose than for all other uses combined. There is a great abundance of copper in the United States, obtained by both underground and open-pit mining. Some of the major copper-producing states are Michigan, Montana, Arizona, Utah, Nevada, New Mexico, Tennessee, and California. The copper mined is of various grades of purity.

Some of the low-grade ore contains only about 1 per cent copper. For this type the first step is to remove some of the impurities; this process concentrates the percentage of copper in the ore to at least 30 per cent. Concentrates and high-grade ore are sent to smelters, where they go through a variety of processes to remove almost all of the impurities. This is done by melting the ore, removing the slag, and then blowing compressed air through the molten mass, with the result that most of the undesirable materials are burned off. The copper comes from the smelters 99 per cent pure, containing very small amounts of gold, silver, and other substances which interfere with its effectiveness as a conductor of electricity. It must therefore go through another process called refining. This is done in an electric cell, where the copper is dissolved and re-deposited on plates as pure copper. This copper is then poured into bars or ingots from which all forms of copper products are made. At this point zinc is added to make brass, or tin added to make bronze. The copper or its alloys are then rolled into sheets and strips or made into tubing, rod, or wire.

Copper and its alloys have many desirable characteristics that make them most useful. They have high ductility and malleability, which enable them to be drawn into wire or hammered into shapes with ease. For this reason, copper is the most desirable art metal for beginners. They also have great resistance to corrosion. The oldest tools and utensils known are made of copper and have defied time and the ages, for they do not rust. Bronze, especially, is used extensively as parts and fittings on ships.

Because of its low cost and because it is second only to silver in its ability to conduct electricity copper has become the foundation of our electrical industry.

From generators, through transformers through wire to our homes, electricity i carried by copper to provide for our com forts and conveniences.

Copper is also an excellent conducto of heat and is used in cooking utensils in heating elements, in furnace system and in many other ways. Copper ha many uses in transportation. Every auto mobile contains 45 pounds of copper anc its alloys or more. Over three millior pounds are used in a single, large steam ship such as the *Queen Mary*. Perhap the greatest tribute to copper as the theme metal for the United States is the famous Statue of Liberty, which is made of 300 separate pieces of sheet copper Copper, of course, is all-essential in military life for ammunition, gun parts, and other implements.

Discussion Topics

1. Why is copper the most important metal in our electrical industry?
2. How is copper ore refined?
3. What characteristics of copper and its alloys make them good art metals?
4. For what other uses is copper especially well suited?

Unit 61. The Story of Aluminum

Aluminum is the wonder metal of this era. You see and use it every day—in the wrappers on your candy bars, in the bridges that you cross, in the containers for your toothpaste, and in jet-propelled aircraft. All of us take the metal for granted; yet less than 100 years ago

aluminum cost over 500 dollars a pound and was considered more precious than gold.

It is the most plentiful of all metals, since bauxite ore, from which it is made, is found in almost every country in great abundance. The problem, however, has lways been to refine the metal from the re. Unlike most other metals, which can be refined directly, aluminum can be obtained only after a long, complicated process of purification and refinement.

Bauxite ore is mined either by the open-pit or by the underground method. The first step is to produce alumina, or aluminum oxide, which is a white powdery substance. This is done by a chemical and physical process of refinement which removes the hydrogen and most of the impurities. Then the second important step, and the most difficult, is to remove the oxygen to secure the metal itself. This is done in an electric cell in a procedure somewhat like charging a storage battery. This electric cell removes the oxygen, leaving the pure metal, which can be drained off. It takes 4 to 6 pounds of bauxite ore, 10 kilowatt-hours of electrical energy, $\frac{3}{4}$ pound of carbon, and many other chemicals to produce 1 pound of aluminum, that sells for a small fraction of a dollar.

This wonder metal has many desirable characteristics. It is light, only about a third as heavy as iron or steel, and it conducts heat readily and quickly, so that it is very useful in electrical work and for cooking utensils. It also resists corrosion. The cap on the Washington Monument is made of aluminum and was placed there in 1844. This metal also reflects heat and light and is, therefore, a good insulating material. It is nonmagnetic and can be worked easily.

Aluminum is not strong enough in its natural state for some uses; so other materials such as copper, silicon, manganese, magnesium, and chromium are added to produce its many alloys. Aluminum has thousands of uses in industrial life.

Discussion Topics

1. In what products is aluminum commonly found?
2. From what ore is it refined?
3. What are the characteristics of aluminum?

Unit 62. Metal Products

Since so many things are made of metal, the more you know about them, the more intelligent will be your selection of projects to construct and of commercial products to buy.

METALS IN HOME CONSTRUCTION

The home of today has much more metal in its construction and in its furnishings than the home built in earlier years. For example, many of the window casements once made of wood are now made of steel or of aluminum. Aluminum window frames and casements have the advantage of requiring little maintenance, since they do not easily corrode except in salt-water areas. They have the disadvantage, however, of being good conductors of heat and cold. Steel casements, on the other hand, are subject to rust and therefore require painting or bonding.

The ducts for heating and air conditioning are usually made of galvanized or galvannealed steel, the latter being the more desirable. Today, much of the duct work is aluminum. It is lighter than steel while retaining a great deal of strength. It will not rust, as does galvanized steel, when exposed to the elements. On the exterior of homes metal flashing is needed on the roof, around windows, and wherever there is danger of leaks. The best type of flashing is made of copper since it is resistant to corrosion and is easily formed. However, most flashing and eaves troughs are made of galvanized or galvannealed steel because of their low cost.

Home Utensils

The pots and pans used in the kitchen are usually made of metal. Aluminum pans are good conductors of heat and cold and are fairly easy to keep clean. However, they should be kept away from strong alkali soap, and soda must not be used in cooking. Also, pans made of aluminum should not be plunged in cold water when they are very hot since this would put them out of shape.

Porcelain and enamel pots and pans are made from thin mild steel coated with porcelain or enamel, which is baked on the steel. The enamel is a glasslike substance. The chief difficulty with this type of utensil is that it stains and chips easily.

Tinware

Few people realize that there is very little tin in tin cans and tinware. Tin cans are, of course, made of tin plate, which is mild steel with a very thin coating of tin. Tinware in pans used as kitchen utensils has a thicker coating of tin than tin cans for once the tin is scratched off, the steel rusts rapidly.

Jewelry and Silverware

Jewelry can be divided into two general groups—that called *costume jewelry*, which is made from the baser metals such as copper, brass, or nickel silver, and *precious jewelry*, made from gold, silver, and platinum. Platinum is the most expensive of all metals and therefore is not so common.

Gold is frequently considered the ideal metal for jewelry because of its rich yellow color. Gold is too soft to use alone; so it is alloyed with silver, copper, zinc and/or nickel. Pure gold is reckoned at 24 carats; thus 10-carat gold would have 10 parts of gold to 14 parts of other metals. When copper is added as one of the alloying metals, yellow gold results. When silver is added, green gold is obtained. Nickel with gold produces white gold, and various other shades from pink to amber are obtained by varying the kind and amounts of alloying materials.

Sterling silver is required by law to contain at least 0.927 part of silver with the other parts consisting of an alloy of copper and other materials. Since sterling silver is so malleable, it can be rolled and shaped into very thin sheets. Therefore, it is not so important that it be stamped sterling as that the gauge be heavy enough to prevent bending.

Coin silver, which is used in much jewelry, especially Mexican and Indian, contains 90 per cent pure silver and 10 per cent other metals. Silver plate is made by shaping the object of some less expensive metal, usually nickel silver or copper, and then electroplating the metal with sterling silver. The quantity of silver plate is determined largely by the amount of sterling silver deposited.

METALS IN AUTOMOBILES

There are so many different kinds of carbon and alloy steels that make up the various parts of an automobile that it would be impossible to list them all here. In addition, many other nonferrous metals such as aluminum, copper, and special nonferrous alloys are all used to produce the modern car. Automobile manufacturers are constantly attempting to develop steels for bodies and frames that are harder, more elastic, more shock-resistant, and of thinner gauges so that the car may be both rigid and light.

Discussion Topics

1. Name as many places as you can in which metal is found in home construction.
2. What metals are used for making kitchen utensils?
3. What is tinware?
4. Of what metals is precious jewelry made?

Section XI. SUGGESTED PROJECTS

BENCH METAL AND WROUGHT IRON

Tie rack. This is an especially useful article to have, and making it provides a good deal of practice in the use of many different hand tools. The design of the ends can be varied. For example, you could cut your initials, a figure, a symbol, or numbers.

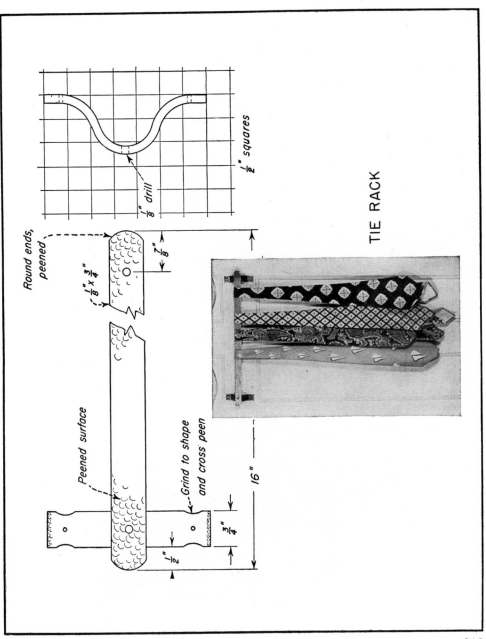

TIE RACK

Small plant holder. Though very simple in construction, this plant holder is surprisingly good looking if made well. It is designed to display small-size plants. The shiny disk is a piece of tin plate; you can cut the disk from a tin can.

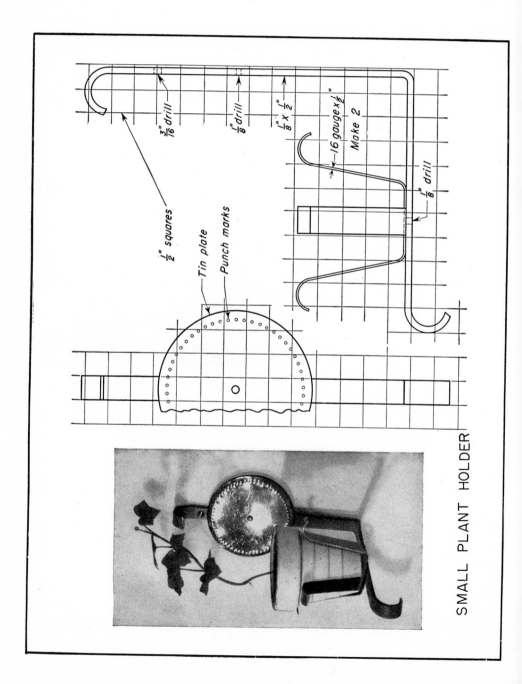

SMALL PLANT HOLDER

Pin-up lamp. A pin-up lamp has always been a popular project to add a final touch to your room. The design of this one is practical because the back holds firmly to the wall and hides the cord. It is not necessary to add the metal stamping. The lamp can be finished by cleaning off the oxide and applying clear lacquer or by painting or enameling.

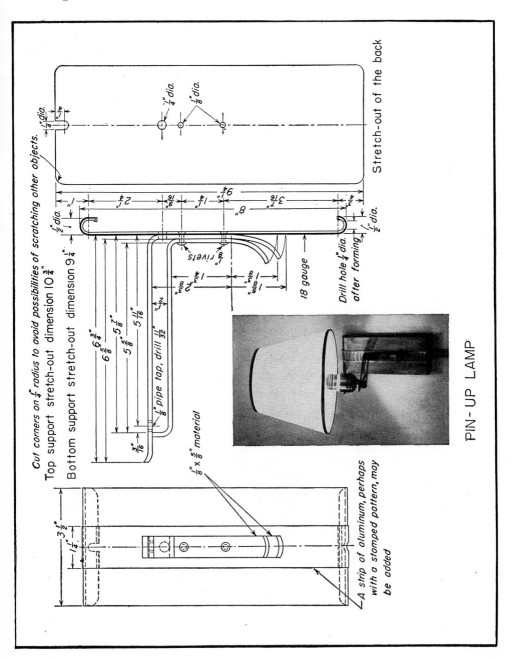

PIN-UP LAMP

Folding clothes hanger. If you do not have enough closet space—and who does?—here is a good idea for getting more. This hanger is especially convenient since it can be folded up and put away when not in use. It is more difficult to make, however, since the parts must be fitted together quite accurately.

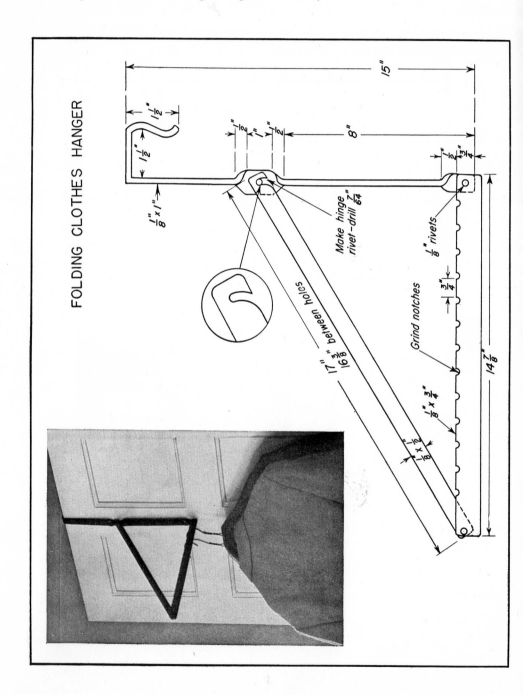

FOLDING CLOTHES HANGER

SHEET METAL

Note pad. This is a good way of combining printing with metalworking. Print your nickname on the note paper and then make this little holder to fit it. It shows that the most elementary projects are frequently the most attractive.

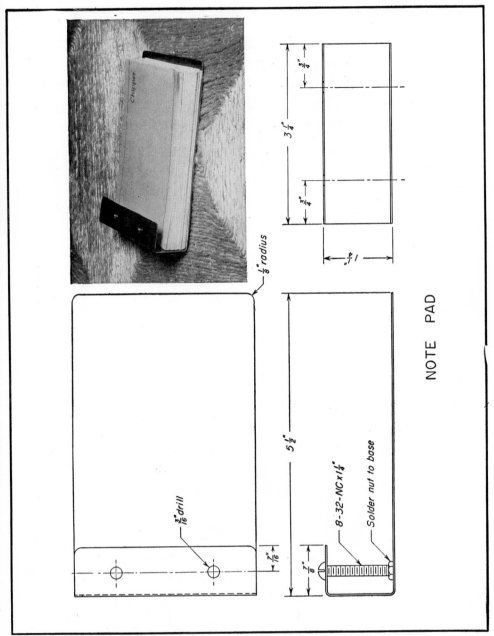

Matchbox holder. Most people still like to use the big, old-fashioned kitchen matches, and this is the ideal way of keeping them within easy reach. Only spot soldering is necessary since the box does not have to be waterproof. This has been painted and decorated with a decal. Cement a piece of sandpaper to the bottom for scratching the matches.

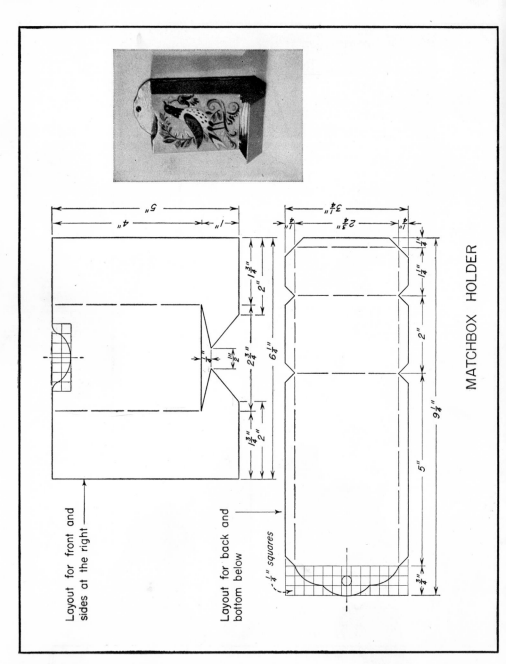

MATCHBOX HOLDER

Dog dish. This is just the right size for a dog-feeding dish, and the construction includes a wire edge, a grooved seam, and waterproof soldering. You will probably want to paint your dog's name on the dish.

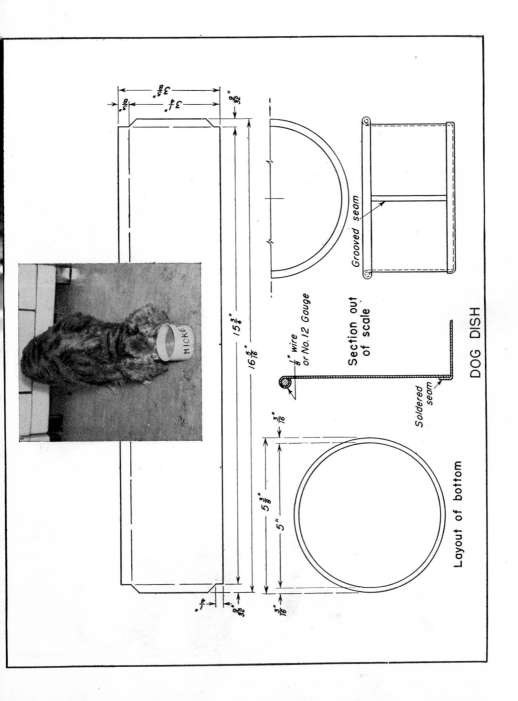

DOG DISH

Watering cans. Here are two suggestions for using tin cans; the taller one is made from a large fruit-juice can and the smaller from a coffee can. The most difficult part in this construction is the soldering. Remember that the paint must be removed wherever parts are to be joined. You can probably think of several interesting things to make from tin cans.

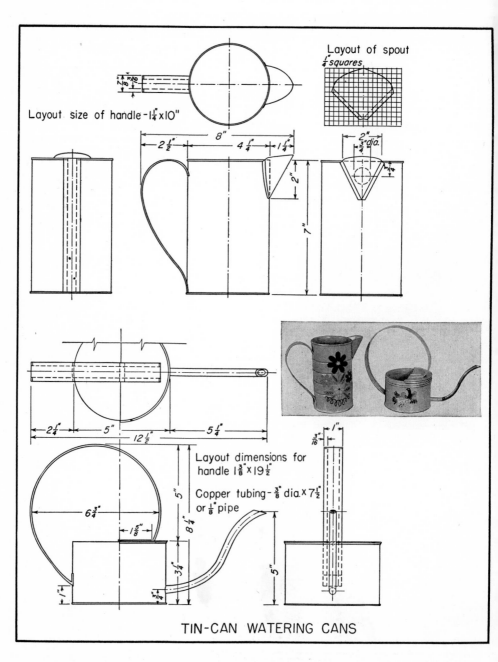

TIN-CAN WATERING CANS

Sheet-metal planter. This shows what can be done to a metal box to dress it up a little. The curved ends are separate pieces, riveted in place. All seams must be soldered to make the box waterproof. This one has been hand-painted. It certainly is obvious here that the finish is important to the final appearance.

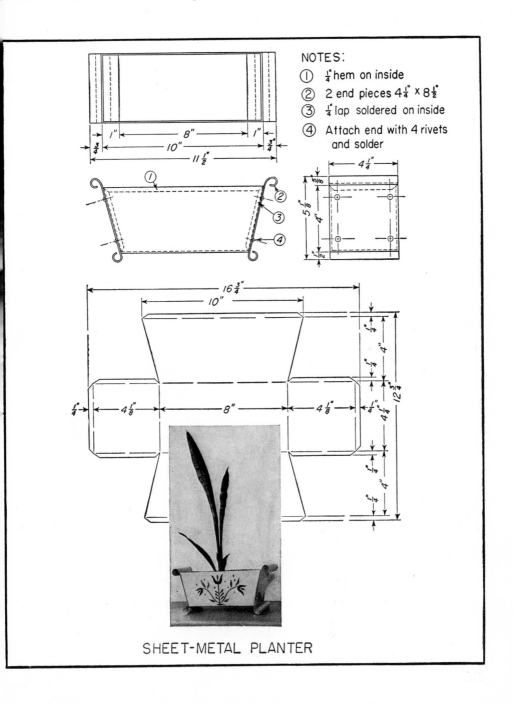

NOTES:

① ¼" hem on inside

② 2 end pieces 4¼" × 8½"

③ ¼" lap soldered on inside

④ Attach end with 4 rivets and solder

SHEET-METAL PLANTER

Letter openers. A good first project for the beginner and one that can very well be designed is a letter opener. Frequently, extra thicknesses of metal are sweat-soldered together to thicken and to strengthen the handle. When this is done, it is a good idea to combine two different metals. Making one of these will give you good experience in metal cutting and surface decoration.

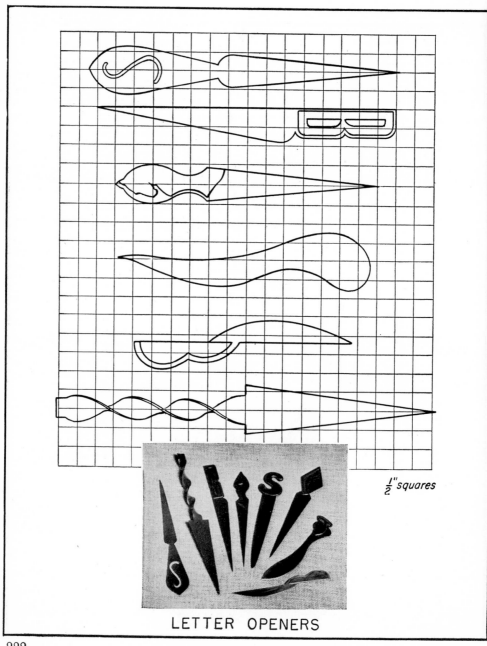

$\frac{1}{2}''$ squares

LETTER OPENERS

Miniature log holder. The handle is made by twisting a thin strip of copper around a rod. The bottom is a single piece with the feet formed by doming. After the bottom is shaped, the handle is soldered in place. It is a copy in miniature of the large log holders for a fireplace and is a wonderful little dish for candy or nuts.

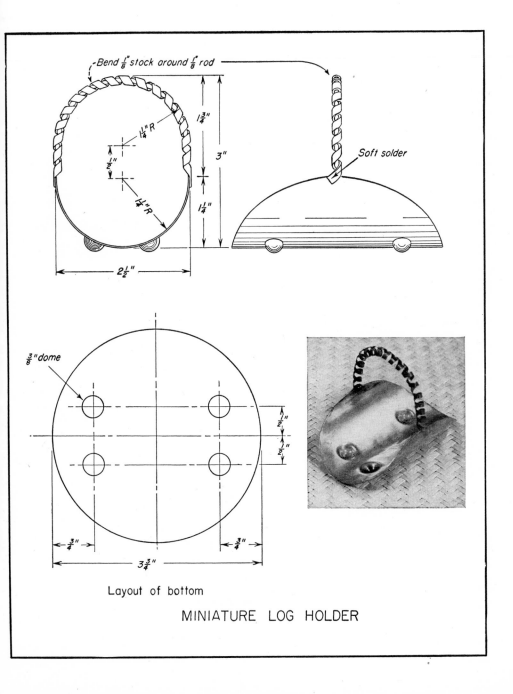

Layout of bottom

MINIATURE LOG HOLDER

Bracelets. Bracelets are always a distinctive and smart art-metal project that can be made in almost an endless variety of designs. The larger one has a brass wire soldered to the copper background. Bracelets can be enriched by overlay, etching, chasing, dapping, planishing, or piercing and the finish made gleaming by polishing and covering with lacquer.

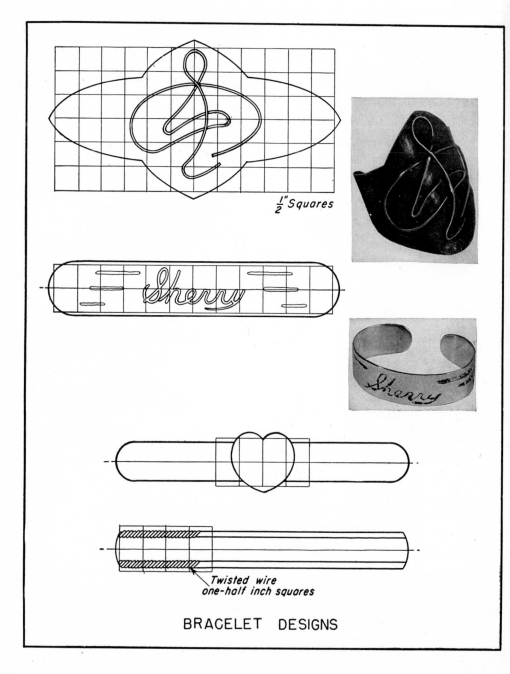

$\frac{1''}{2}$ *Squares*

Twisted wire one-half inch squares

BRACELET DESIGNS

Small trays. Here are only a few of the many shapes of small trays it is possible to form by sinking or beating down. Notice that the simpler the design is, the more handsome the tray is. The entire surface may be peened or just the center. The edges may be chased, fluted, flared, or embossed.

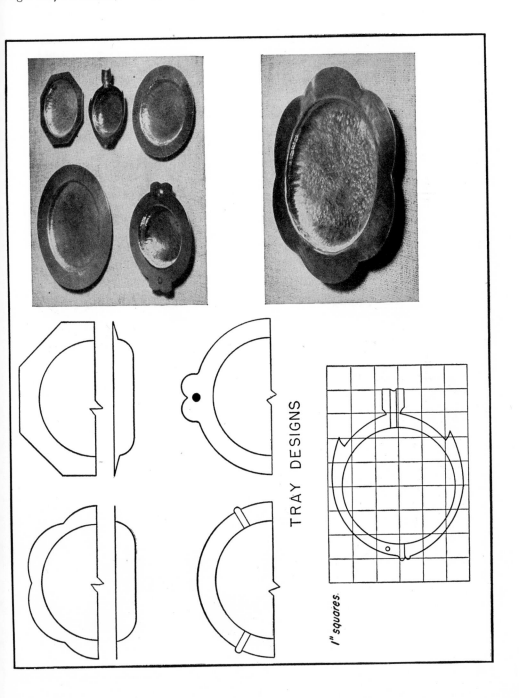

TRAY DESIGNS

I" squares.

Copper jewelry. Small bits of copper and brass are all that is necessary to make many pieces of jewelry and art metal. The identification tag for a key ring would make a good first project. Your initials could be tapped out in the center. Everybody would like to have a tie clip or a small pin to keep or to use as a gift.

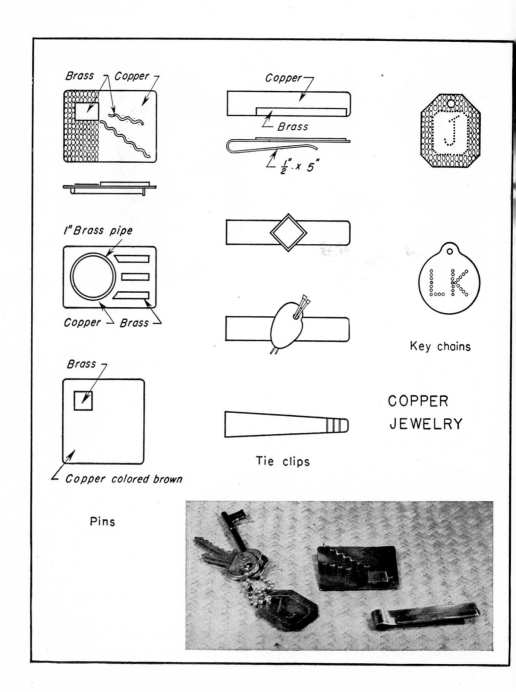

Brass · Copper

Copper · Brass

1" Brass pipe

Copper · Brass

Brass

Copper colored brown

Pins

Copper · Brass

$\frac{1}{2}" \times 5"$

Tie clips

Key chains

COPPER JEWELRY

Sterling jewelry. Four projects made in one of the author's jewelry classes: a ring made of flat sheet and decorative wire (a small hole must be drilled in the back of the ring for soldering the top in place), a pin with connecting chain, a pair of pendant earrings, and a set of cuff links. Most jewelry requires that fittings be purchased and hard-soldered in place.

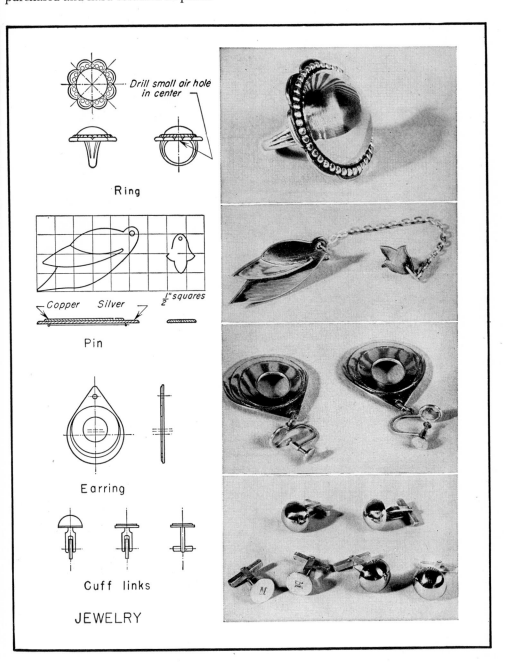

Ring

Drill small air hole in center

Copper   Silver $\frac{1}{2}$" squares

Pin

Earring

Cuff links

JEWELRY

Pastry server. A gracefully designed server made from nickel silver, this project is decorated across the handle with a small piece of fancy sterling-silver wire, that has been hard-soldered in place. Its beauty is in its simplicity.

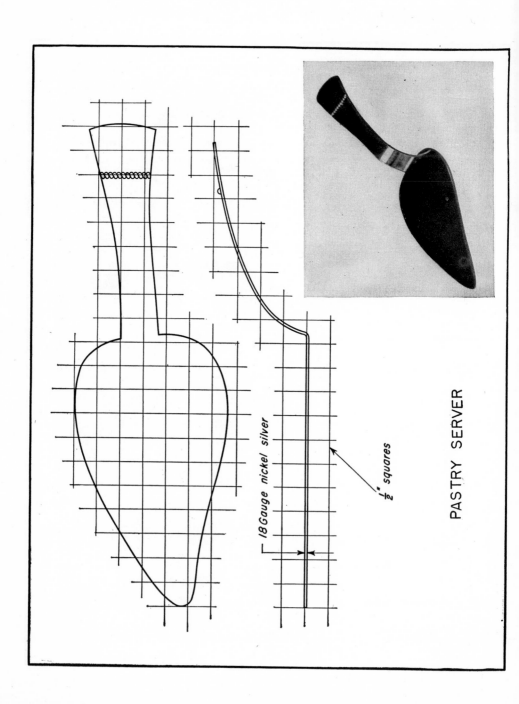

18 Gauge nickel silver

½″ squares

PASTRY SERVER

Modern lamp. A graceful lamp made of brass tubing and sheet with a free-form, flower-like base. The rod is hard-soldered to the base to make it secure. In making a lamp, always start with the shade and scale the lamp to it in size and design.

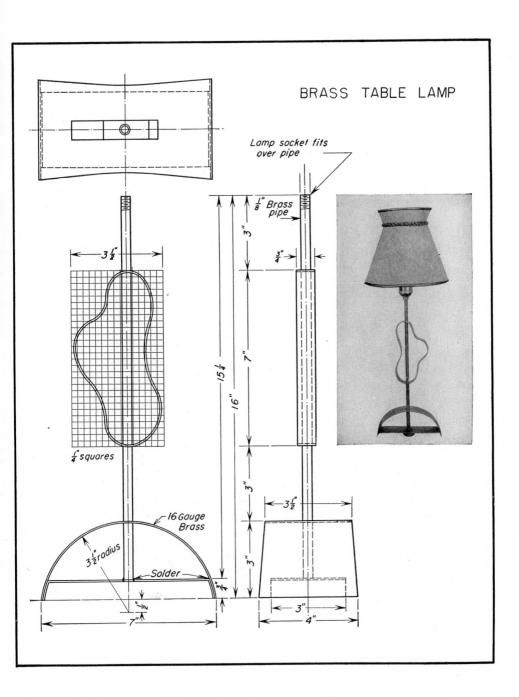

BRASS TABLE LAMP

Lamp socket fits over pipe

$\frac{1}{8}''$ Brass pipe

$3\frac{1}{2}''$

$\frac{1}{4}''$ squares

16 Gauge Brass

$3\frac{1}{2}''$ radius

Solder

7"

$15\frac{1}{4}$

16"

7"

3"

$\frac{3}{4}''$

3"

3"

$3\frac{1}{2}''$

3"

4"

FORGING

Center punch and cold chisel. These are good beginning projects in forging. They involve simple fundamentals and elementary heat-treating. The picture shows some other projects you can make for your own tool chest. (See Machine Shop drawings.)

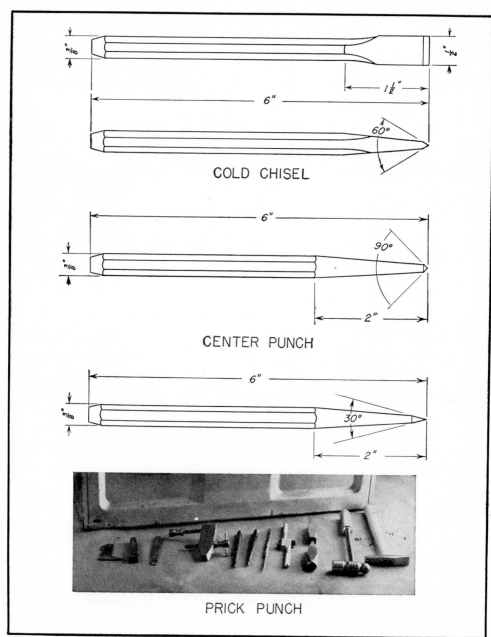

COLD CHISEL

CENTER PUNCH

PRICK PUNCH

Fireplace set. One, two, or all of these articles would be most useful to have near the fireplace. The small shovel has many other practical uses. Making this set calls for forging of a decorative kind.

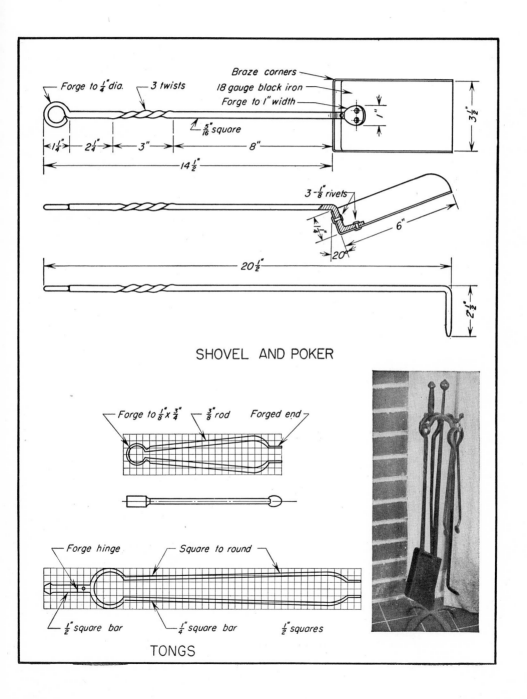

SHOVEL AND POKER

TONGS

Plant holder. This unusual plant holder requires very artistic work. It is assembled by welding or brazing the rods together. This area should be covered with a small piece of copper or brass. The leaves are also brazed to the rod.

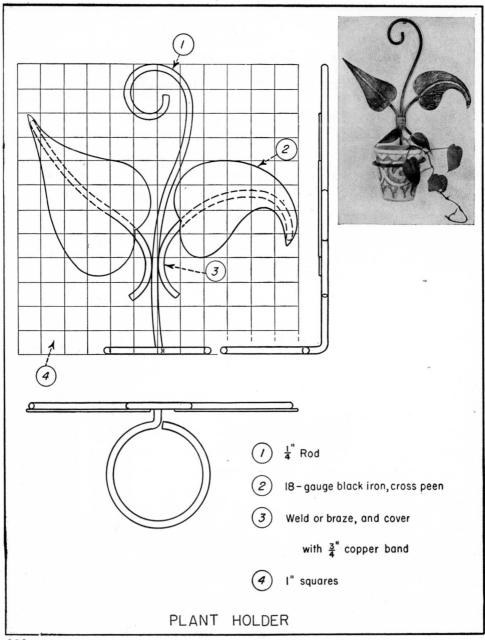

1 $\frac{1}{4}$" Rod

2 18-gauge black iron, cross peen

3 Weld or braze, and cover

    with $\frac{3}{4}$" copper band

4 1" squares

PLANT HOLDER

Stapler. Every organization, club, office, or small print shop needs a stapler that will assemble programs and booklets. This is a good welding exercise, which will result in a very useful stapler that will assemble books as large as 8½ by 11 inches. The stapler itself must be purchased, part of the base cut off, and the stapler section fastened to the welded base.

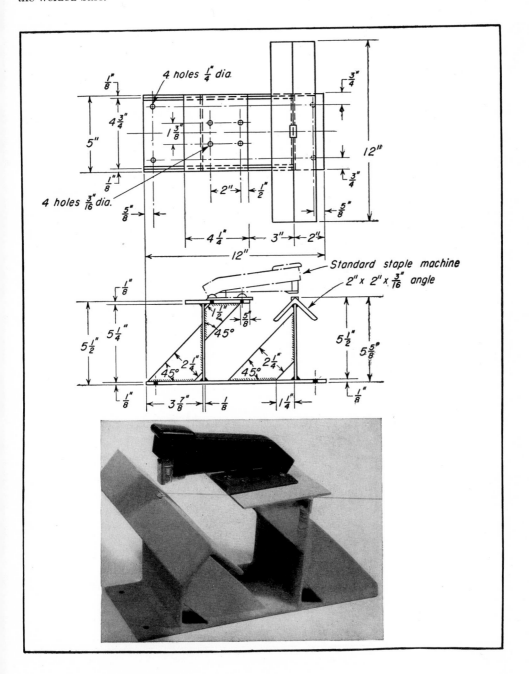

MACHINE SHOP

Scriber. Every real craftsman, mechanic, engineer, designer, inventor, or builder, must have his own tool chest. You cannot make all of your own tools, but one way to become interested in possessing a set of your own is to make a few. A good lathe project to begin with is a scriber.

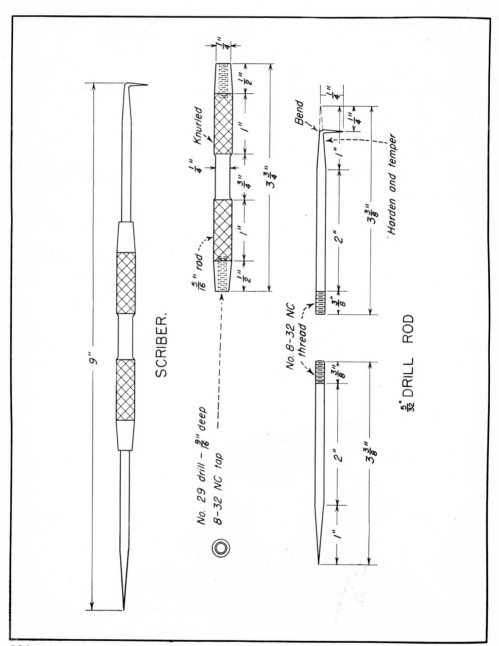

Ball-peen hammer. Another handy tool that can be made on the lathe. The threads to join the head to the handle can be cut with a tap and die or on the lathe.

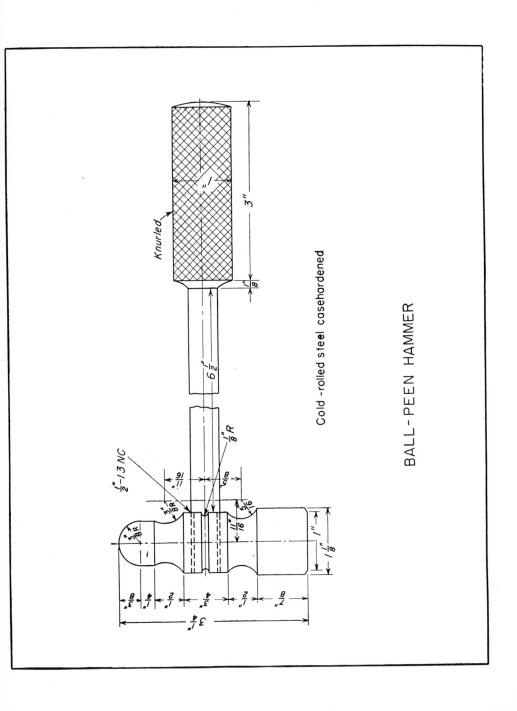

BALL-PEEN HAMMER

Cold-rolled steel casehardened

Riveting hammer. This is an ideal project with which to start your shaper experience. It's another very useful tool to have in your chest.

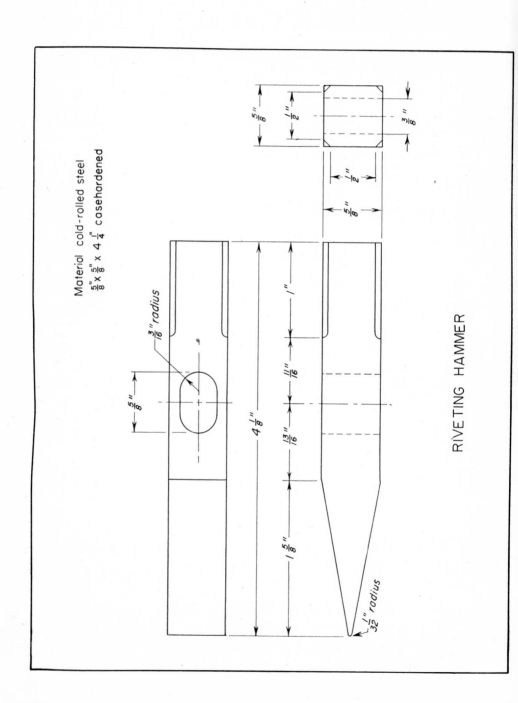

Tap wrench. If you plan to do advanced work in machine shop, you will have good use for this tool. Making it involves many of the fundamentals of bench metal and machine shop.

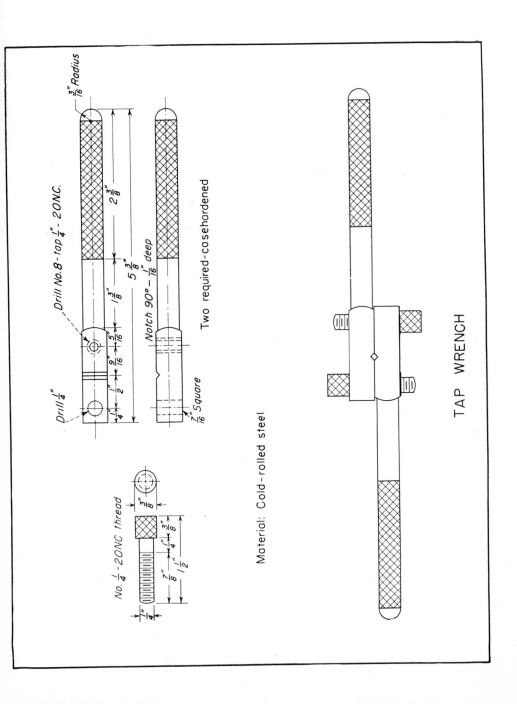

TAP WRENCH

Paper punch. For the more advanced machine-shop student, this punch makes an excellent project. It requires careful fitting of parts.

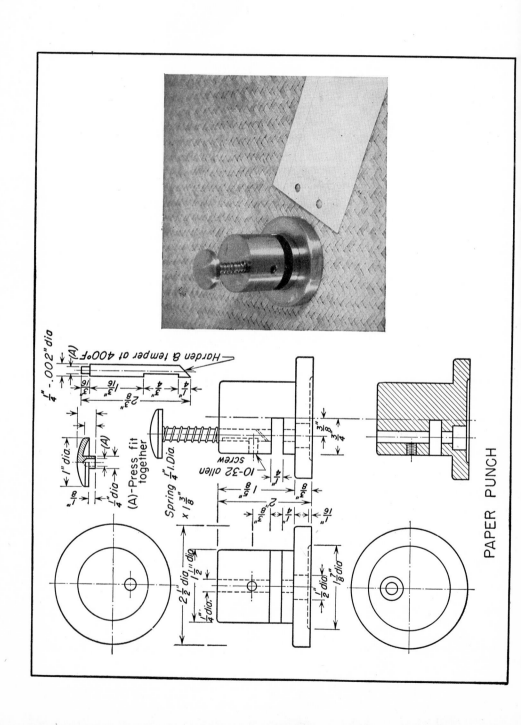

PAPER PUNCH

Brass and plastic hammer. This hammer is a simple machine-shop tool, and just the thing for the art-metal worker, machinist, or auto mechanic. The head is two-thirds brass and one-third plastic.

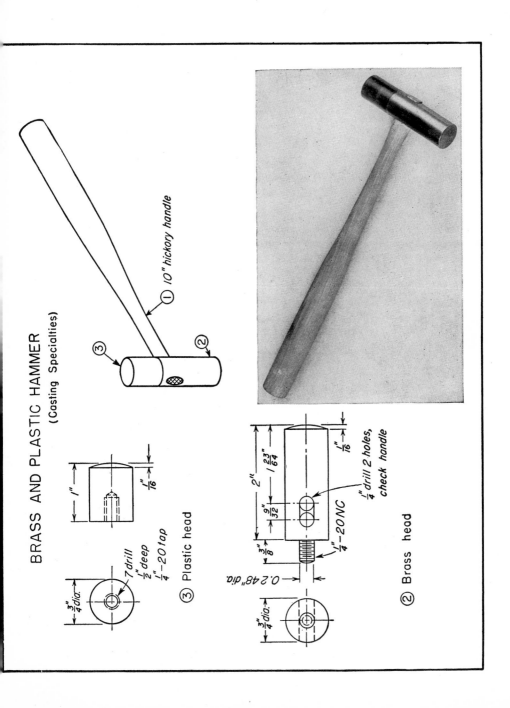

BRASS AND PLASTIC HAMMER
(Casting Specialties)

① 10" hickory handle

③ Plastic head

② Brass head

7 drill
½" deep
¼"–20 tap

¾" dia.

1"

1/16"

0.248" dia.

3/8"

2"

1 23/64"

9/32"

1/16"

¼"–20NC

¼" drill 2 holes, check handle

¾" dia.

Correlated List of Visual Aids

The visual materials listed below and on the following pages can be used to supplement the subject matter of this book. We recommend, however, that each film be reviewed before using in order to determine its suitability for a particular class or group. Each film has been listed only once—in relation to the section to which it is most applicable. However, in many instances, a film may be used advantageously in the study of other sections of this book.

Both motion pictures and filmstrips are included in this list of visual materials, and the character of each one is indicated by the self-explanatory abbreviations "MP" or "FS." Immediately following this identification is the name of the producer; and if the distributor is different from the producer, the name of the distributor follows the name of the producer. Abbreviations are used for the names of producers and distributors, and these abbreviations are identified in the list of producers and distributors (with their addresses) at the end of the bibliography. In most instances, the films listed in this bibliography can be borrowed or rented from local or state 16mm film libraries. A list of such libraries, compiled by the U.S. Office of Education and entitled *A Directory of 2,002 16mm Film Libraries,* can be purchased for a nominal price from the Superintendent of Documents, U.S. Government Printing Office, Washington 25, D.C.

Unless otherwise indicated, the motion pictures listed in this bibliography are 16mm sound films, and the filmstrips are 35mm silent.

Section I—Metalworking

Centering Small Stock (MP USOE/UWF 12min). How to locate the centers of round, square, and rectangular pieces of stock. Supplementary filmstrip (34 frames), same title, also available. (Machine-shop work series. Bench work.)

Language of Drawing (MP Mc-Graw 10min). Explains the necessity for a knowledge of mechanical drawing, the common language of the building world. (Mechanical-drawing series.)

Reading a Three-view Drawing (MP USOE/UWF 10min). How to use a blueprint to visualize the object; interpret a blueprint; and make a tool block according to specifications. Supplementary filmstrip (30 frames), same title, also available. (Machine-shop work series. Blueprint reading.)

241

Sectional Views and Projections, Finish Mark (MP USOE/UWF 15-min). Dimension, center, cross-section, and object lines; projection of a sectional view; uses of finish marks; and meanings of standard cross-section lines. Supplementary filmstrip (29 frames), same title, also available. (Machine-shop work series. Blueprint reading.)

Shop Procedures (MP McGraw 17min). Shows how finished drawings are used as detailed instructions in all steps of manufacturing. Supplementary filmstrip, same title, also available. (Mechanical-drawing series.)

Simple Calculations for Flat Layouts (FS USN/UWF 64 frames). How to calculate and lay out flanges, bends, heads and seams on metals.

Visualizing an Object (MP USOE/UWF 9min). How a blueprint is developed; dimensions shown by different views; and various kinds of lines used on a blueprint. Supplementary filmstrip (29 frames), same title, also available. (Machine-shop work series. Blueprint reading.)

Section II—Bench Metal and Wrought Iron

Cutting Threads with Taps and Dies (MP USOE/UWF 19min). How to use a hand die to cut threads on a stud to fit in tapped holes. Supplementary filmstrip (48 frames), same title, also available. (Machine-shop work series. Bench work.)

Drilling in Metal, Wood, and Plastics (MP USN/UWF 21min). Six basic drilling steps; how to lay out wood and

plastics with drill press, electric and hand drills.

Filing (MP USN/UWF 15min). Importance of files and filing in metalworking; filing techniques; various types of files and file cuts.

Fundamentals of Filing (MP USOE/UWF 12min). How to care for and handle files; clean files; and select different files for different metals. Supplementary filmstrip (52 frames), same title, also available. (Machine-shop work series. Bench work.)

Laying Out Small Castings (MP USOE/UWF 16min). How to lay out holes for drilling; locate a reference point; use hermaphrodite calipers, combination square, and surface gauge. Supplementary filmstrip (32 frames), same title, also available. (Machine-shop work series. Bench work.)

Scraping Flat Surfaces (MP USOE/UWF 14min). Handscraping flat surfaces to a surface plate; five common forms of hand scrapers; operation and care of the flat scraper. Supplementary filmstrip (33 frames), same title, also available. (Machine-shop work series. Bench work.)

Section III—Sheet Metal

Blanking Sheet Metal on the Squaring Shear (MP USOE/UWF 15min). How to lay out tapered blanks on an aluminum sheet; use hold-downs and treadle; check blanks and trim blanks. Supplementary filmstrip (59 frames), same title, also available. (Aircraft work series. Blanking sheet metal.)

Blanking Sheet Metal with Hand Snips (MP USOE/UWF 18min).

How to cut along a straight line; cut an outside circle, a notch, an inside line; and remove burrs left by cutting. Supplementary filmstrip (45 frames) same title, also available. (Aircraft work series. Blanking sheet metal.)

Filing Template Metal (MP USOE/UWF 15min). How to file a square edge and remove burrs; rotate the wrist for filing inside curves; file inside rectangle; and remove fillets from corners. Supplementary filmstrip (39 frames), same title, also available. (Aircraft work series. Templates.)

Finish Forming by Hand (MP USOE/UWF 16min). Successive stages of forming with a flat fiber strip; shrinking large wrinkles with a forming tool; marking excess metal with a surface gauge; and checking finished work with a contour template. Supplementary filmstrip (38 frames), same title, also available. (Aircraft work series. Forming sheet metal.)

Forming on a Hand-operated Brake (MP USOE/UWF 17min). How to set up the brake for bend angle and bend radius; operate the brake; check test pieces and finished work. Supplementary filmstrip (51 frames), same title, also available. (Aircraft work series. Forming sheet metal.)

Making a Master Contour Template (MP USOE/UWF 18min). How to transfer a line from a lines board to a piece of sheet metal; measure and record bevel angles. Purpose of a master-contour template and the need for accuracy. Supplementary filmstrip (34 frames), same title, also available. (Aircraft work series. Templates.)

Sawing Template Metal (MP USOE/UWF 17min). How to mount a saw blade on a band saw; select and adjust blade guides; saw to a layout line; chew out metal from a notch; and remove burrs. Supplementary filmstrip (50 frames), same title, also available. (Aircraft work series. Templates.)

Spot Welding (MP USOE/UWF 20min). How to spot-weld parts of an access cover; set up the machine; remove and install electrodes; set pressure, current, and time controls; test the set-up; and clean the electrode tips. Supplementary filmstrip (44 frames), same title, also available. (Aircraft work series. Assembling and riveting.)

Section IV—Art Metal and Jewelry

Decorative Metal Work (MP Brandon 10min.) Detailed explanation and visualization of the making of an etched bracelet. (Produced in cooperation with the Universal School of Handicrafts.)

Hand Soldering (MP USOE/-UWF, 20min). Theory of soldering; how to prepare soldering irons and torches; clean and prepare the work; solder wire and lug joints; and seal seams. Supplementary filmstrip (52 frames), same title, also available. (Accessory-assembly series. Tools and procedures.)

Metal Craft (MP EBF, 11min). How a master craftsman makes a pewter bowl, a bronze bowl, and a jewel box.

Section V—Forging

Forge Welding (MP USOE/UWF, 12min). How to heat mild steel for forging; upset and scarf round stock; make a lap weld; and hammer-refine the weld. Supplementary filmstrip (26 frames), same title, also available. (Farm work series. Forging.)

Forging with a Hand Forge (MP USOE/UWF 13min). How to clean the tuyere and build an open fire in a forge; lay out and mark the stock; heat mild steel for forging; and forge an eye. Supplementary filmstrip (48 frames), same title, also available. (Farm work series. Forging.)

SECTION VI—HEAT TREATING

Heat Treatment of Steel: Elements of Hardening (MP USOE/UWF, 15-min.) How steel is quench-hardened; how the structure and hardness of steels with different carbon content change at progressive quench-hardening stages; an iron-carbon diagram. Supplementary filmstrip (40 frames), same title, also available. (Engineering series. Heat-treatment of steel.)

Heat Treatment of Steel—Elements of Tempering, Normalizing, and Annealing (MP USOE/UWF 22min). How steel is tempered; how the structure, toughness, and hardness of plain carbon steel change at progressive tempering stages; how steel is normalized and annealed. Supplementary filmstrip (31 frames), same title, also available. (Engineering series. Heat-treatment of steel.)

SECTION VII—FOUNDRY

Molding with a Loose Pattern (MP USOE/UFW 21min). Introductory film showing principles of foundry work. Animation and live-action photography. Supplementary filmstrip (37 frames),

same title, also available. (Foundry work series. Bench molding.)

NOTE: The U.S. Office of Education has 13 other motion pictures, each with an accompanying filmstrip, on various aspects of foundry work. For a list of titles and film descriptions, write to either the U.S. Office of Education or to United World Films.

SECTION VIII—WELDING

Oxyacetylene Welding Light Metal (MP USOE/UWF 21min). How to assemble a gas welding outfit; adjust gas pressure; adjust the flame; make a butt weld and a T weld. Supplementary filmstrip (41 frames), same title, also available. (Welding-procedures series. Oxyacetylene welding.)

SECTION IX—MACHINE SHOP

The Drill Press (MP USOE/UWF 10min). Functions, characteristics, and basic operations of the drill press. Supplementary filmstrip (32 frames), same title, also available. (Machine-shop work series. Basic machines.)

The Lathe (MP USOE/UWF 15-min). Functions, characteristics, and basic operations of the engine lathe. Supplementary filmstrip (49 frames), same title, also available. (Machine-shop work series. Basic machines.)

The Milling Machine (MP USOE/UWF 15min). Functions, characteristics, and basic operations of the milling machine. Supplementary filmstrip (41 frames), same title, also available. (Machine-shop work series. Basic machines.)

Safe Practices in Metalworking: Engine Lathe (FS Handy). Series of 11 filmstrips with following self-explanatory titles:

1. *Kinds—Parts—Safety* (70 frames)
2. *Operating—Speeds* (78 frames)
3. *Carriage Controls—Feeds* (81 frames)
4. *Turning Tools* (83 frames)
5. *Chucks—Chucking Work* (95 frames)
6. *Centers—Setting Tools—Facing* (90 frames)
7. *Center Holes—Mounting Work—Facing between Centers* (75 frames)
8. *Turning between Centers—Shouldering* (81 frames)
9. *Recessing—Chamfering—Filing—Polishing—Knurling* (80 frames)
10. *Taper Turning—Threading* (91 frames)
11. *Collets—Faceplates—Rests* (85 frames)

The Shaper (MP USOE/UWF 15min). Functions, characteristics, and basic operations of the shaper. Supplementary filmstrip (40 frames), same title, also available. (Machine-shop work series. Basic machines.)

NOTE: The U.S. Office of Education has more than 100 films on various machine tools and other aspects of machine-shop work. For a catalogue of these films write to the U.S. Office of Education or to United World Films.

SECTION X—METALS IN EVERYDAY LIVING

The Drama of Steel (MP USBM 34min). Uses of steel; historic and modern production methods; modern open-pit mining and furnaces; processes in various types of mills, cold-reduction, tin-billet, and bar mills.

Magnesium: Metal from the Sea (MP USBM 23min). Designer's dreams of tomorrow made possible by magnesium; production processes; industrial and domestic uses.

Story of Copper (MP USBM 34-min). Prehistoric uses of copper; open-pit mining and underground mining in Arizona; milling, smelting, and electrolytic refining.

This Is Aluminum (MP USBM 29min). Mining and preparation of aluminum; fabrication of metal and its alloys; demonstration of versatility and suitability for fabrication; display of manfactured articles.

NOTE: The U.S. Bureau of Mines has between 50 and 75 films on metals and metallurgy. Write to the Bureau of Mines for a free catalogue of its films.

Sources of Films Listed

Brandon—Brandon Films, Inc., 1700 Broadway, New York 19, N.Y.

EBF—Encyclopaedia Britannica Films, Inc., 1150 Wilmette Ave., Wilmette, Ill.

Handy—The Jam Handy Organization, 2821 East Grand Blvd., Detroit 11, Mich.

McGraw—McGraw-Hill Book Co., Text-Film Department, 330 West 42nd Street, New York 18, N.Y.

USBM—U.S. Bureau of Mines, 4800 Forbes Street, Pittsburgh 13, Penna.

USN—U.S. Department of the Navy, Washington 25, D.C.
Films released for civilian educational use through U.S. Office of Education and sold, under govern-

ment contract, by United World Films; may be borrowed or rented from 16mm film libraries which have purchased prints.

USOE—U.S. Office of Education, Washington 25, D.C.

Films sold, under government contract, by United World Films; may be borrowed or rented from 16mm film libraries which have purchased prints.

UWF—United World Films, Inc., 1445 Park Ave., New York 29, N.Y.

Sales distributor for many U.S. Government films.

Index